Saturnus
Plumbum.        ♄ · ♄ · Lead

Jupiter
Stannus.        ♃ · ♃ · Tinn.


Mars
ferrus.         ♂ · ♂ · Ironor
                        Steele

Sol.
Aurus.          ☉ · ☉ · Gould.

Venus.
Cuprus.         ♀ · ♀ · Copper.


Mercurius       ☿ · ☿ · Quicks-
                          silver

Luna.
Argentus        ☾ · ☽ · Silver.


Mercurius
Sublimatus.     ☿ · Quicksilver
                    Sublimed.

*S1*

# the arts of the alchemists

Frontispiece: *A page from Salomon Trismosin's* Splendor Solis, *a series of drawings showing Mercurius as the homunculus performing the work within the alembic*
Endpapers: *Alchemical symbols and their interpretations taken from a seventeenth-century copy of the Cantilena of George Ripley*

C. A. Burland

# the arts of the alchemists

THE MACMILLAN COMPANY · NEW YORK

Published in the United States by The Macmillan Company, New York, 1968
Library of Congress Catalogue Card Number: 68-10841

© 1967 by Weidenfeld and Nicolson Ltd

Printed in Great Britain

To the Memory of

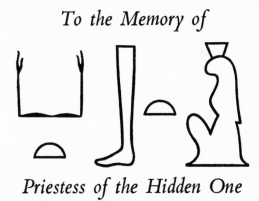

Priestess of the Hidden One

# contents

| | List of Illustrations | xi |
| | Foreword | 1 |
| 1 | Materia Confusa | 4 |
| 2 | Calcination | 20 |
| 3 | Aqua Ardens | 28 |
| 4 | Sublimation | 36 |
| 5 | Condensation | 45 |
| 6 | Crystallization | 69 |
| 7 | Albification | 78 |
| 8 | Solification | 94 |
| 9 | Nigredo | 115 |
| 10 | The Dark Journey | 124 |
| 11 | The Inner Space | 139 |
| 12 | The Words of Power | 155 |
| 13 | Gold from the Blackness | 183 |
| | Conclusion | 207 |
| | Bibliography | 211 |
| | Index | 217 |

# ıllustrations

BEGINNINGS OF ALCHEMY (*pages 9 to 13*)

Egyptian drawing from the papyrus of Nestanebanshru (xxıst dynasty) (*British Museum*)

Etruscan engraved bronze mirror, third century BC (*British Museum*)

Cover page of the *Codex Brucianus:* MS Bruce 96 (*Bodleian Library*)

Model of Alexandrian alchemical workshop (*Science Museum, London*)

*The Gold-making of Cleopatra*, a third-century AD Coptic papyrus, now in Leiden (*Science Museum, London*)

ALCHEMY OF THE EAST (*pages 13 to 16*)

Two pages from a seventeenth-century Arabic treatise, *Uyan al Haka ik* (*British Museum*)

Two pages from a seventeenth-century Arabic commentary by al-Jildaki (*British Museum*)

Hebrew manuscript of an Arabic work on Jewish philosophy (*British Museum*)

Two pages from a seventeenth-century copy of *Al Misbah* by Aidamir al-Jildaki (*British Museum*)

Treatise attributed to Tankalushah the Great, written in Indian script, dated 1807 AD (*British Museum*)

MEDIEVAL FRANCE (*pages 49 to 64*)

Six pages from *Speculum Humanae Salvationis*, an illustrated Biblical commentary of the fourteenth century: MS Latin 511 (*Bibliothèque Nationale*) (photos: F. Foliot)

The Tour Saint-Jacques (photo: French Government Tourist Office)

Engraving of Saint-Jacques-la-Boucherie (Bibliothèque Charcornac)

Title page of *Alchimie de Flamel:* MS Français 14765 (*Bibliothèque Nationale*) (photo: F. Foliot)

Seventeen pages from *Alchimie de Flamel:* MS Français 14765 (*Bibliothèque Nationale*) (photos: F. Foliot)

ARTISTS AND PATRONS OF ALCHEMY (*pages 81 to 88*)

Sections from three of the four *Ripley Scrowles*, Lübeck 1588: MSS Add. Sloane 5025 (*British Museum*)

Title-page of Ripley's *Cantilena:* MS Ashmole 1445 (viii) folio 2 (*Bodleian Library*)

Opening pages of Ripley's *Cantilena:* MS Ashmole 1445 (viii) folios 2v and 3r (*Bodleian Library*)

Pages from a seventeenth-century copy of the *Cantilena:* MS Ashmole 1394, folios 156, 157 (*Bodleian Library*)

Three pages from Salomon Trismosin's *Splendor Solis* (1582): Harleian MSS 3469, folios 25, 26, 27 (*British Museum*)

Portrait of Rudolf II, Holy Roman Emperor (*Reproduced by gracious permission of Her Majesty the Queen*)

The 'Street of the Alchemists', Prague (*Orbis CSSR*)

THE SEVENTEENTH CENTURY: COMMENT AND ILLUSTRATION (*pages 105 to 112*)

*The Alchemist* from *Proscenium vitae humanae . . .* by Johann Theodor de Bry, Frankfurt, 1627 (*British Museum*)

An alchemical laboratory *c.* 1650, engraving by le Bas (*Science Museum, London*)

Frontispiece of *Theatrum Chemicum Britannicum*, collected with annotations by Elias Ashmole, London, 1652 (*British Museum*)

Five pages from Thomas Norton's *Ordinall of Alchimy*, in *Theatrum Chemicum Britannicum*, London, 1652 (*British Museum*)

Two pages from Michael Maier's: *Secretioris Naturae Secretorum Scrutinium Chymicum*, Frankfurt, 1687 (*Science Museum, London*)

THE SEVENTEENTH CENTURY: DRAWINGS (*pages 129 to 136*)

Ten pages of emblematic figures in red chalk from a seventeenth-century work. MS Sloane 1. 1316 (*British Museum*)

Eight pages from *Cabala Mineralis Rabbi Simeon ben Cantara*, with watercolour drawings and text in English and Latin: MS Add. 5245 (*British Museum*)

LAMBSPRINGK (*pages 145 to 152*)

Series of plates from Lambspringk: *De Lapide Philosophico, figurae et emblemata*, in *Musaeum Hermeticum reformatum et amplificatum*, Frankfurt, 1678 (*British Museum*)

THE SEVENTEENTH CENTURY: LATER WORK (*pages 161 to 168*)

Van Dyck: Portrait of Sir Kenelm Digby (*Reproduced by gracious permission of Her Majesty the Queen*)

Series of twelve plates from Basilius Valentinus: *Practica una cum duodecim clavibus*, in *Musaeum Hermeticum reformatum et amplificatum*, Frankfurt, 1678 (*British Museum*)

First page of Lully: *Hermes Bird* from *Theatrum Chemicum Britannicum*, London, 1652 (*British Museum*)

Final page and vignette of *Liber Patris Sapientiae*, in *Theatrum Chemicum Britannicum*, London, 1652 (*British Museum*)

THE EIGHTEENTH CENTURY AND AFTER (*pages 185 to 200*)

Vignette from the title-page of vol. II of *Bibliotheca Chemica Curiosa*, (ed. J. J. Mangetus), Geneva, 1702 (*British Museum*)

# Illustrations

Illustrations from a paper by Sendivogius in *Bibliotheca Chemica Curiosa*, Geneva, 1702 (*British Museum*)

Series of fifteen plates from *Liber Mutus alchemiae mysteria filiis artis nudis figuris evidentissime aperiens* in *Bibliotheca Chemica Curiosa* (ed. J. J. Mangetus), Geneva, 1702. This work was first published at La Rochelle in 1677 under the title *Mutus Liber in quo tamen tota Philosophia hermetica figuris hieroglyphicis depingitur* . . . (*British Museum*)

Notice of a transmutation in Prague from the *Bibliotheca Chemica Curiosa*, Geneva, 1702 (*British Museum*)

The alchemist's furnace, from *Bibliotheca Chemica Curiosa*, Geneva, 1702 (*British Museum*)

Medal struck from alchemical gold on 31 December 1716 (*Kunsthistorisches Museum, Vienna*)

Medal struck from alchemical silver transmuted by J. J. Becher in 1675 (*Kunsthistorisches Museum, Vienna*)

Specimen of alchemical gold, from an unknown source (*British Museum*)

NOTES ON THE COLOUR PLATES

*frontispiece*

Folio 23 from *Splendor Solis* (1582) by Salomon Trismosin: Harleian MSS 3469. This page is part of a series of drawings showing the Work being performed within the alembic; Mercurius as the homunculus is inflaming and heating the dragon in the process of calcination (*British Museum*)

*facing page 1*

Silver gilt dish of the Roman period, found with buried treasure at Chaourse, Aisne, France. Diameter: approx. 12 inches; date: *c.* third century AD. It displays the technical skills of the metal technicians of the classical world, whose practical recipes formed a basis for many alchemical studies in later times (*British Museum*)

*facing page 24*

The Lycurgus Cup, probably made by Italian craftsmen in the fourth century AD. The subject of the designs is part of the Dionysian Mysteries and the cup, which looks like green chalcedony outside, glows red when lit from inside. It was made by blowing a special glass containing finely divided gold powder within a mould, and then carving and undercutting the figures. The combination of magic and high technical skill in the preparation of the gold-glass mixture is also part of the classical basis from which the alchemists derived their procedures and theory (*British Museum*)

*facing page 40*

A section of the first *Ripley Scrowle*, painted in Lübeck in 1588. The seven processes of the alchemist, shown here as a monk, are linked here to the whole Work, shown as a red essence of the Stone. The figure of the homunculus within the vessel is Mercurius in his various transformations (*British Museum*)

*facing page 72*

A section of the fourth *Ripley Scrowle*. The Melusina descends on the tree of life to bring wisdom to Man and Woman. Around the fountain of living waters are the alchemical philosophers. This picture makes a statement which suggests that the search for alchemical knowledge is a reversal of the sin of Adam and Eve (*British Museum*)

*facing page 96*

Folio 24 from Trismosin's *Splendor Solis* (1582): Harleian MSS 3469 (*British Museum*)

*facing page 120*

Section from the Egyptian Papyrus of Taweniu of about 1000 BC, representing the separation of earth and sky at the Creation. The green earth-god Geb is the active power which brings fertility to the black earth (the *massa confusa* of the alchemists); the sky-goddess Nut is the protective power of nature. In such beliefs are the origins of the Hermetic mysteries. (*British Museum*)

*facing page 176*

Folio 29 from Trismosin's *Splendor Solis* (1582): Harleian MSS 3469 (*British Museum*)

The author and publishers would like to thank the institutions and photographers mentioned above for their kind permission to reproduce the illustrations. All printed books and objects, apart from manuscripts, in the British Museum were photographed by J. R. Freeman and Co. (by courtesy of the Trustees). The layout of the illustrations is by Shashi Rawal.

# the arts of the alchemists

# foreword

Alchemy is a subject of which we have all heard, and which is yet a mystery. In some ways it belongs to the world of mystery stories from the past. We remember perhaps the shade and wonderful light of Rembrandt's etching of the alchemist, or the stories we read in Chaucer or Ben Jonson. Was the alchemist a philosopher, deep in a mysterious study where he discovered the secrets of transmutation? Was he just a charlatan involved in a particularly fantastic kind of mumbo-jumbo? Was he simply a forerunner of the scientists of today? Or had he an occult knowledge which we cannot hope to acquire in our materialist environment?

The alchemist was all these things in the eyes of his contemporaries. We look at his books and marvel at the beauty of the illustrations, the care with which they were written, and the obscure allusions of the language. Yet when we begin to delve deeper we find a world of philosophy which almost amounts to a religion. The wise old man with his crucibles and furnaces also had his learned books which served to guide him in his experiments. He was impressed with the need to develop his own personality until he was in touch with the whole world of creation. The final revelation of the secret knowledge came with suddenness. The alchemist firmly believed that a power from above had enlightened him at the moment when he was at last fit to receive the knowledge. The making of gold was thought of as a seal of approval set on a lifetime of work and study. In terms of our civilization those ingots of alchemical gold were produced at an expense far in excess of the material value of the metal.

Yet for the alchemist there was a fascination which led him on. The journey of exploration was not so much a chemical process as a search for the inner meaning of the whole material universe. The quest brought its own satisfaction. The alchemist made a contribution to the knowledge of the human mind as great as his contribution to the development of scientific chemistry.

I

*Silver gilt dish of the Roman period, found in France; the skills of early metal technicians formed a basis for many later alchemical studies*

In this book we shall seek out the story of alchemy. In spite of the alchemists' belief that the methods they used in their laboratories were the same as those of their forerunners right back to the strange Hermes Trismegistus, we can see that the 'Spagiric Art', as the alchemists called it, did develop through the centuries. To some extent the basic document, *The Emerald Tablet*, on which they said all their knowledge rested, had its origin in ancient Egyptian mysticism. The later developments filtered through to wise men in the outside world, and crystallized in that great meeting place of wisdom, the *Museion* in Alexandria. Thence the ideas spread through the Roman Empire. After Rome fell, the wisest of the Arabs continued the study of this curious scientific philosophy. Then in turn the European scholars of the Middle Ages learnt from the Arabs, and brought their own scholastic interpretations to the subject. During the Renaissance thought was influenced both by the revival of ancient mystical beliefs and by the urge for practical results, so we can trace a new path of exploration which leads to the development of a Christian mysticism such as that of Jakob Boehme, and also to the development of science through such men as Sir Isaac Newton.

To accompany the alchemist in the study of his mysterious art is fascinating, because we follow a group of people who have transmitted to our modern times some of the knowledge and mystery of the ancient world ... a philosophy so ancient that we can only guess at its true origins.

It is fitting here to conclude our introduction with a translation of the words with which the studies of all good alchemists began. They were said to have been given by Hermes Trismegistus (the Egyptian god Tehuti, Lord of Wisdom) to Maria Prophetissa, who many say was the beautiful Miriam, sister of Moses.

IT IS TRUTH; TRUTH WITHOUT LIES; CERTAIN TRUTH
THAT THAT WHICH IS ABOVE IS LIKE THAT WHICH IS BELOW:
AND THAT WHICH IS BELOW IS LIKE THAT WHICH IS ABOVE
TO ACCOMPLISH THE MIRACLES OF ONE THING.

AS ALL THINGS CAME INTO BEING BY THE CONTEMPLATION OF ONE
SO ALL THINGS AROSE FROM THIS ONE THING,
BY A SINGLE ACT OF CREATIVE ADAPTATION.

> The Father thereof is the Sun.
> The Mother is the Moon.
> It was carried in the womb by the Wind.
> The Earth is the nurse.

It is the father of all works of wonder throughout the world.
It is perfect in power.
If it be cast on earth it will divide the element of Earth
From the element of Fire:
The subtle element from the gross matter.
In its great wisdom it ascends gently from Earth to Heaven.
Again it descends to earth.
Then unites in itself the force from Things Above
To the force from Things Below.

Thus thou shalt possess the glory of the brightness of the whole world.
All obscurity and darkness shall fly from thee.
This thing is the might and power of all strength.
It will overcome every subtle thing
And has the power to penetrate every solid substance.
THUS WAS THE WORLD CREATED.

For this reason I am called *Hermes Trismegistus*
I hold three parts of the wisdom of this world.
That which I have to say about the operation of Sol
Is completed.

One may read this document in many ways; for the Alchemists it was their charter for a voyage of discovery in which we hope to join them. True, our scientists have achieved transmutations of elements in atomic laboratories at great expense. Yet with all these intellectual victories behind us we have not yet found the key to that other alchemy which would set free the shining gold of the spiritual possibilities of mankind. We should consider whether we have opened the doors of knowledge for the benefit of material-minded 'puffers', or whether we should continue the search for that 'gold which is not the common gold'. As we shall see in the following pages there is no easy answer.

# 1

# materia confusa

Alchemy has no definable beginning. Its first texts are Hellenistic and mostly Alexandrian. Before them lay most of the existence of the human race, within them lay the influences of all the many people who had contributed to the mixed intellectual climate of the eastern Mediterranean in Hellenistic times. The period when the Ptolemies were ruling Egypt was a time of intellectual ferment. Persian, Jewish, Greek and Egyptian philosophies were constantly producing new and attractive amalgams. There was debate on philosophical matters to such an intense degree that riots and murder sprang from it. Each ephemeral school of thought was sure that it held the ultimate truth and so its teachings must supersede all others. The wisest were those who did not shout their wares in the market place, and who worked within their own communities of friends to try to understand the secrets of the universe which they realized as both within and outside their personalities. To contemplate that of which one is a part was not an easy or happy task, yet then, as in our own times, such an understanding was felt to be an imperative necessity. It is not unnatural that Alexandria became the focal point of such studies. It had contacts with all the trade routes of the ancient world, so that the roads there were easy, and in its heart there was the finest collection of material for study, in the *Museion* and the library. One cannot imagine this focal area of Hellenistic knowledge as peaceful. It was never so. Seaport, tourist town, commercial emporium, banking centre, home of political intrigue and centre of all mystery in the form of religious speculation, Alexandria must have been a bustling, confusing place for the scholar. Yet nowhere else could he find such riches of knowledge and understanding.

The sources of the alchemical path were many. It became a necessary way of thought once man had mastered the strange process of applying heat to certain kinds of rock and thereby changing its nature into dross and shining metal. Then came the other wonder of mixing two metals in a fluid state and so producing a new metallic alloy which had different characteristics from either of its parents. Some metals tarnished and could be restored to health by washing with various vegetable juices. All could be purified by a renewed passage through the fire, by melting and burning away the dross, or by heating and beating until the impurities flaked away as swarf. The king of metals was the first known because it had no alloys in nature but was found in glistening golden grains in streambeds. Even when it was melted like other metals, it remained itself, brilliant, sun-like gold. It did not corrode with time, it could not be dissolved by any ordinary acid, it was irresistibly beautiful and adorned all who wore it. Because it was rare and beautiful it obtained a great value in the eyes of men, and in ancient times gold was sold by barter for many fine things, so that its possession became the symbol of power and wealth. It became symbolic of royal power as simply and as naturally as it was linked with the sun in the minds of men.

Throughout history there have been many discoveries of gold in many independent places, and copper, tin and silver, as well as platinum, were discovered apparently quite independently by the American Indian peoples of Peru and Colombia. One may speculate endlessly, and without much advance, about the association of metals with natural forces and gods. The result of this association was important in alchemy becase the metals became associated with the planets. In the case of copper the association with Venus is probably due to the association of the metal as well as the goddess with Cyprus, and so with the Aegean world of thought. One finds no trace of this link in Peruvian traditions. However, silver was associated with the moon both in ancient America and in Europe. Its whiteness was probably the major part of the reason for the link, but we also have to remember that silver is usually found in association with the common heavy dull lead. The difference of melting point and hardness probably marked silver out for some special attention and its comparative rarity brought it up in value as a near equal to gold. It was almost naturally the moon compared to the sun, the queen next to the king of metals.

The association of iron with Mars is obviously a late one, since iron, apart from meteoric supplies, was a late discovery. Apparently it dates from only a little before 2000 BC and from the region of the Caucasus, where the people probably found it when using some high temperature fuel such as oak wood or when smelting in high windy regions. The ancient astrologers of Mesopotamia had identified Mars as Nergal, the war god. Perhaps this was linked with the colour of the planet, which was like a distant fire, or from its resemblance to a shining bronze spear head. It must have been later when the Iron Age had developed its weapons of the new metal that the transference of iron to the metal of Mars took place, and Venus took over the attractive copper as her metal.

It appears, then, that in the early days of metallurgy the associations of metals with the planetary deities was not derived from immediately apparent, natural associations except in the case of gold and silver. The rest of the series of parallels between metal and planet bears all the evidence of having been made under the influence of learned astrologers rather than any natural compulsion of primitive tribal philosophers and medicine men. The systems adopted by all later alchemists must be regarded as the result of much intellectual comparison between metals and planets on the part of highly trained priestly specialists living in a civilized community.

As civilization progressed in the Mediterranean area, mercury was distilled from cinnabar, and so provided another mystery of the metal which was a liquid, and which could enter a mysterious amalgam with other metals and yet be distilled away from them. The changeable nature of this liquid metal made it easy to pair it with the rapid alternations of little Mercury, who was identified with that magical personality Hermes, messenger of the gods.

The foregoing suggests that wherever alchemy developed it must have been in the eastern Mediterranean. In no other place could the right mixture of philosophy and technical knowledge be found.

The basic philosophies within alchemy grew as religious customs. They are so often linked with astronomy that we may be certain that Babylonian religion lay in the background. Thought about the planetary spheres and the hierarchies of creative power is all strongly Semitic and goes back to the thought of the Middle East long before the definition of the *Kabbalah*. The ideas of ritual and many of the theories of creation evident in alchemical thought must belong to the world of Egyptian speculation. As we have seen, even the famous *Emerald Tablet* is so linked with Egyptian thought that it would be easier to ascribe it to an Egyptian priestly college than to alchemists.

Even the early texts which the alchemists regarded so highly as the foundations of their art are shown by E. J. Holmyard to contain recipes for gilding, and the preparation of alloys does not necessarily imply that the search for the Philosopher's Stone really concerned the production of pure gold for material purposes. It may well be that these texts are really portions of technical treatises which have been adopted by philosophical writers because they contained phrases which fitted in well with the religious beliefs which they were teaching.

In spite of all disappointments when seeking the true roots of alchemy we can find an enduring line in both Greek and Egyptian thought. This is an understanding of the philosophy of the nature of the universe. The basic thought of matter being called forth from a primeval *massa confusa*, like the black earth of Egypt when the Wisdom of God pronounced words of power, is the seed of all alchemy. That is the fruitful spark in *The Emerald Tablet*, and it is attributed to Hermes, who is also equivalent to Ṭehuti, who is the wisdom of God personified as a being with the poetic symbol of an ibis head. Indeed, the spirit of poetic symbolism is also a root of alchemical methods of expression. The changes in the state of ore and metal are seen as a picture of the development of the human person as well as of the universe. The result was hoped to be a certain state of perfection in which, in all the orders of nature concerned, the result was the development of the greatest perfection compared to gold.

This knowledge of the way to perfection was a typical half-secret doctrine expounded openly by books and writing, yet in such terms that the initiate alone could unravel the true meaning. In Ptolemaic Egypt, as in all the Middle East, this attitude was characteristic of the priesthoods who taught many ceremonies and kept them written down in archaic systems of writing, both cuneiform and hieroglyphic, which could no longer be read by the untaught mass of the citizens. The whole mystique of the period was one of hidden knowledge which could be revealed through initiation and ceremonial observances to the dedicated neophyte who wished to follow the secret paths of salvation. He would become transmuted into a purified personality. This was equally characteristic of the Eleusinian mysteries, where the initiate was expected to show forth his new perfection by the good sense of his conversation and by his calm bearing during the vicissitudes of ordinary life.

The Egyptian contribution, then, was an early myth based on the appearance of new life under the influence of the sun from the Nile mud. This was never lost through all the centuries of development of Egyptian thought. The gods were perpetually manifest in the events of nature as well as in the temple ceremonies. From Alexandria came a new group of ideas which developed a Greco-Egyptian religious cult of Asar-Hap or Serapis. Greek philosophy and mystery cults were linked reasonably well with the Egyptian systems. Alexandria was also a meeting place of the nations. There was a Persian military settlement there, groups of Syrian traders and teachers, occasional visitors from India to Carthage, and a very large Jewish community who gathered in a pleasant seaside quarter and built a gigantic synagogue in which they worshipped in peace. Thus, in the one great city there were all the lines of thought which could develop into the full mysticism of the alchemists. There were also technicians in glass and metal work who had all the basic practical science which persisted almost unchanged for a thousand years.

The unifying centre was the *Museion* in Alexandria. The first Ptolemies had worked very hard to build the city and equip it with facilities far in advance of any other city of its time. In particular, Ptolemy Philadelphus encouraged learning and by any means in his power acquired books for his wonderful House of the Muses. The building was equipped for reading and copying, for quiet study, and for comparison of objects and specimens of the material world with the written works of the past. There is nothing quite like it in the modern world, though it must have been somewhat akin to the British Museum in London. In the Alexandrian *Museion* during its eight centuries of existence we find sufficient cause for all the work that alchemy ever performed, and the fostering of all the heresies and philosophies of its age.

The Greek contribution to the learning which became alchemy was a process of reasoning quite different from the native Egyptian empiricism and poetic magic. The Greeks had already produced philosophers and mathematicians of importance who had been interested in the structure of the universe. They had arrived at the theory of an atomic structure of matter, and decided for themselves that there must be some elemental structure. Without our means of precise analysis it was quite impossible for the philosopher to comprehend the complexity of the true atomic system. To him the atom was the smallest possible particle of any substance. The basic substances were thought of as being varying mixtures of basically elemental aspects of nature.

The theoretical elements were Earth, Air, Fire and Water. This is a quite reasonable description of nature when we consider it. Take any material at all and heat it on a metal plate; it will give off moisture, the watery element, then it will give off air, or gas as we should call it, then it will probably set off a rush of fire, and finally we shall be left with a heap of burnt earthy material. That is the empirical basis of the old reasoning about the elements. We should know it because it is the basis of all the chemistry of the alchemists. Following the ancient Greek way of thought one should be able to vary the elemental combination of substances and create matter. To a person with this point of view, it was only too easy to take the empirical work of metallurgists, who where seeking to perfect the colour of bronze or to find a good system for gilding, to be a method of adjusting the combinations of matter so as to produce higher materials.

Aristotle, who died ten years after the foundation of Alexandria, set the pattern for future reasoning about matter by his linking of qualities with the

# Beginnings of Alchemy

Egyptian drawing of XXIst Dynasty (*c.* 1000 BC) from the papyrus of
Nestanebanshru showing Tehuti (Thoth) standing before Ra Hormachis
wearing symbols of creation on his head. Throughout the history of alchemy
Thoth was regarded as Hermes Trismegistus

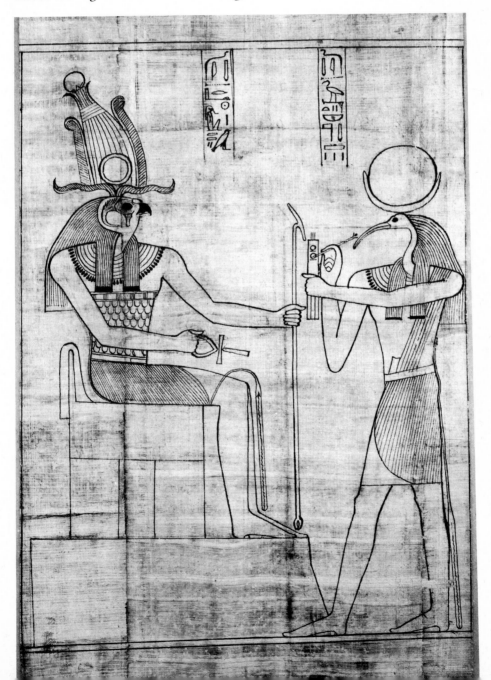

Engraved bronze mirror, Etruscan,
from third century BC showing
Mercury, Venus and other deities
whose images persist throughout
alchemical history

The cover page of the *Codex Brucianus*,
showing a fusion of the ancient
Egyptian symbol for life with the
Christian cross. The manuscript
contains a Gnostic treatise including
alchemical data

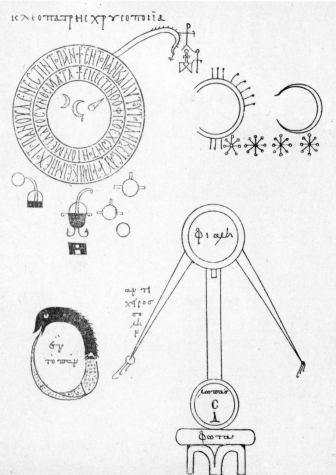

*Above:* Reconstruction model of an alchemical workshop at Alexandria in the beginning of the Christian era

*Left:* Kleopatra Chrisopoeia: *The Gold-making of Cleopatra.* A Coptic papyrus of the third century AD now in Leiden. The serpent is inscribed 'One is All'. The double ring reads: 'One is the Serpent which has poison according to two compositions', and 'One is All, and through it is All, and by it is All', and 'if you have not All, All is Nothing'. Note the drawing of the Kerotakis, and symbols of moon and planets

*Opposite:* Greek alchemical apparatus for distillation and digestion

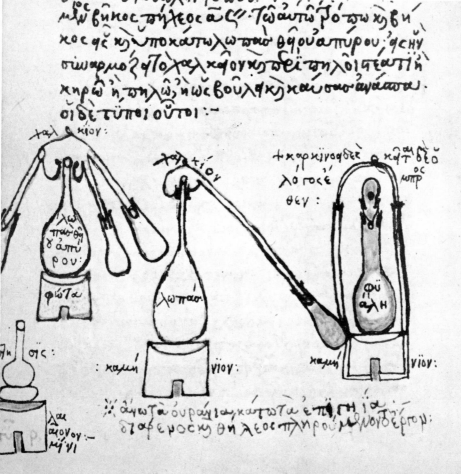

بسم الله الرحمن الرحيم يسرو يسير
الحمد لله الاولى الا وله قبله الاخير اخذ
بعده خالق كل شيء اذا شاء الاله الاحوال
الموجود الواحد المعبود وصلواته على
خير خلقه وعلى الرضى عنهما بعد فاذ صنفت
هذا الكتاب ذاكره على صناعة الطب
والحكمة وعملها من الهيولى التي تنتفع
العمل بها بعد اقامة الدليل على امكان الصناعة
وذكرت الكم والكيف جلا ومفصلا ثم اثبت
كل فصل بشهادات من اقوال الفلاسفة
ليكون مواقفا لهم وضمت الكتاب مفصلا
من ماهية الرمز واعربت عن كيفيتها لتسهل
للقارى حل اشكالها ومعضلاتها وجعلتها وكل
كله في خمس جمل تشتمل ها تسع عشر فصلا
الجملة الاولى تشتمل خمس فصول
الفصل الاول في موضوع علم صناعة الحكمة
الفصل الثاني يشتمل على امكان زوال العرض

الداظر

ولا يد النحوية كح صدرابيات الشذ وله
...

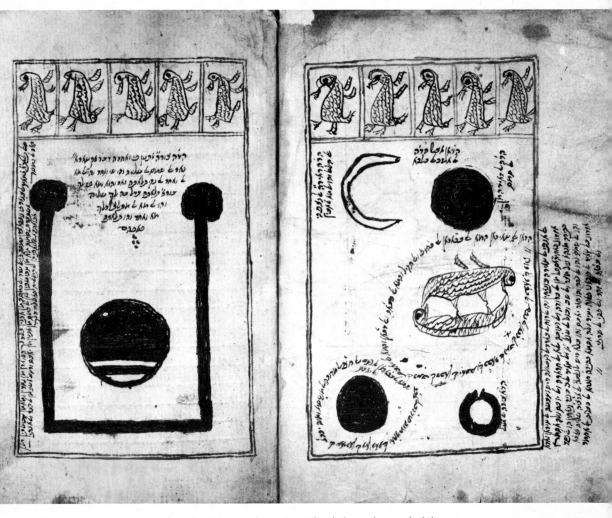

Hebrew manuscript of an Arabic work on Jewish philosophy and alchemy, showing symbolic designs said to have been seen in a ruined temple in Egypt. Note the symbols of sun and moon and the union of Above with Below, which have alchemical significance

*Opposite above:* A seventeenth-century Arabic treatise on alchemy: *Uyan al Haka ik*

*Opposite below:* Kala'id al Nuhur, a seventeenth-century Arabic commentary by al-Jildaki

*Al Misbah*, a seventeenth-century copy of a treatise on alchemy by Aidamir al-Jildaki, who died in 743 AD

Treatise on alchemy attributed to Tankulushah the Great, written in Indian script and dated August 1807 AD. This page deals with the preparation of alchemical materials

On washing the materials & calcination

Calcination of Gold

Litharge Purified

elements. Heat, Cold, Dryness and Fluidity can be combined with Earth, Air, Fire and Water in degrees of consonance and assonance which greatly enrich the original ideas. The Aristotelian theme is often expressed by a square which is drawn from the mid-points of the sides of a circumscribing square. It often appears as a symbol in later works. In fact Aristotelian ideas about the nature of matter persisted among the educated public for nearly two thousand years because they seemed eminently reasonable, and there was simply no scientific apparatus which could be used to check them. It is no wonder that the alchemist worked in the spirit of the four elements and the four humours; every man of learning was committed to that kind of reasoning.

It is probably true to say that there was no real 'school' of alchemists in Ptolemaic Egypt, or even in any part of the Roman Empire. Yet from Alexandria flowed the amalgam of ideas which could later be sorted out from the confused mass to make a unified concept possible. But we must remember that the philosophy which dealt with the nature of man's relationship to the universe was always the basic point from which all experiments took their origin. Everything which the later alchemists tried came from the basic philosophy of the classical world, and was really an extract from the scattered ashes of learning which remained at the beginning of the dark age after the burning of the *Museion* at Alexandria.

The syncretism of Roman religion helped the spread of Hermetic doctrines throughout the Empire. In Ptolemaic times these ideas had developed from the wisdom-teaching of the ancient priesthood of Egypt. In Roman times these became a special group of ideas developed within religious societies which aimed at the attainment of individual salvation for their members. There was no single body of students of either alchemy or salvationism. The worship of Serapis was accompanied by the deeper and richer emotional worship of Isis, of which Apuleius speaks so movingly in his *Golden Ass*. There were all manner of astrological cults as well, and we find the symbols of planets which later became alchemical symbols scattered round the Latin world. We do not hear of the Roman equivalent of the 'puffers' of the Middle Ages, for the technicians who worked in precious metals were likely to work on a practical basis for material gain through their trade, and not to become philosophers. They had written texts for the members of their guilds and standards of technical ability which were used to hold a good position for their members in the social world; but they did not usually mix philosophy or esoteric religion with their craft. The protective deities of craftsmen were usually aspects of the official state religion and in no sense were they regarded as wonder-working spirits who turned out works of art beyond human capacity for their worshippers. The mystery side of trade guilds in Roman times was very much the mystery by which skilled craftsmen have protected their craft from dilution by unskilled labour throughout all history.

Apart from the obvious philosophical ideas within the Roman Empire there were other currents of belief around its borders which influenced later alchemical thought in Europe. The mythology of both Celt and Norseman held stories of the sacred fires of rebirth, and wonderful stories of the dragons and fire-serpents who protected the inner treasures of the earth. One cannot read the alchemical literature of the Middle Ages without being constantly reminded of the pre-Christian mythology of the peoples to the north of Rome. This is perfectly natural since these tribes were the ancestors of the warriors of the so-called Dark Ages, who rebuilt another kind of civilization on the strong foundations of Roman tradition. The medieval inheritance added a certain romantic beauty of symbolism to the rationality of the classical scholars.

In the Far East there was a totally different development of alchemical ideas linked with goldenness as an expression of the search for enlightenment of the personality. There was little correspondence with European thought on the subject, except insofar as psychological reasons give rise to similar visions and thoughts in both religions. However, a few direct ideas must have been exchanged not only by rare direct contacts through trade, but in particular through the spread of the early Christian heresy of Manichaeism. This was of Persian origin, but spread in Europe, especially in France, where it became the Albigensian movement, and also eastwards into China where there developed a strong Manichaean Church. A philosophical link was present for centuries without direct travel between the two regions.

Thus by the time of the fall of Rome and the rise of the Han dynasty in China, the world was equipped with several philosophical disciplines which had sufficient scientific ideas within them to give rise to alchemical thought. The formulations of the ideas are quite well expressed, but nowhere with such detail as arose when the classical world was replaced by medievalism and the rule of tradition. Confusion of many ideas was replaced by a discipline based on unproven assumptions.

The alchemical idea was bound to arise from observation of the world and the life of the human being, as soon as metallurgy was developed. The processes of change in the development of a metal are singularly like the typically archetypal dreams of middle age in which one's youthful personality is seen as something which is burnt up and sent on a long voyage before resurrection. That such visions fall into place in many myths need occasion no surprise. What is remarkable is that the development of a metal through the ancient processes of smelting and refining was parallel in so many ways. The deficiency of technical knowledge among philosophers contributed to much confusion. But in the ancient world all was ready for the full development which was to follow. When the development of metallurgy was tied to the Aristotelian ideas of the nature of matter, a bridge was made by which the thinker could reconcile the process which should ultimately result in the development of the most perfect of metals, pure gold, with the interior process by which the soul would be purified as in a fire and be reborn perfected, as it were, as pure spiritual gold.

There was a third stratum stemming from the ancient religious philosophies which linked the theme of development both with the rhythm of nature and also with the creative function of sex. But once the philosophic side developed, the symbolism of the ancient nature religions was itself subjected to a system of sublimation. Nevertheless it is present in ritual and art, though not often overtly in alchemical discussion. Perhaps that is natural, since the true alchemist was a special kind of person, probably too intellectual in many ways, who was seeking what he considered to be a higher goal than the everyday facts of life. Hence there was a degree of repression of eroticism in his life which in later times is compensated for in his pictorial explanations of the art.

# 2

# calcination

Fire swept the western world in the dark centuries. First the tribes on the borders of the Roman Empire, rising in the scale of civilization, became strong enough to use the knowledge gained in mercenary service to infiltrate and even assume control of great areas. Next came the great irruption of the Huns from the Asian steppes. Their immense numbers and superiority in cavalry tactics shattered the whole of tribal Europe. Whole nations fled from the advancing armies. Some became conquerors themselves, driving their western neighbours in turn to flee and fight until the coming and going of armies was the central fact of life as far as western Britain.

In the Western Empire Aetius the Consul shattered the frontal advance of the Huns, but beyond the Rhine was a land no longer European. It was part of the immense transcontinental command of the great Attila. The struggles of those days are enshrined in myths such as the grim story of the end of the Nibelungs and the brave, sad tale of Artorius in Britain.

The Vandals swept from the north to sack Rome and set up a kingdom in Algeria and Morocco. The Goths went everywhere, and finally made a rich barbarous kingdom in Spain. But behind a barrier of rivers and mountains the Byzantine Empire held firm and a powerful nucleus of learning and high civilization remained.

The main confusion of the West was due to its defencelessness from the pressures coming from the great plains to the east. This set up a wave of peoples seeking any possible means of movement west and south. The western parts of the Roman Empire were no longer centres of learning. They were survival areas around the Frankish Kingdom and the Goths in Spain. The African Vandal kingdoms fell to the Byzantine commander Belisarius. Thus a little trade from Byzantium reached the West even in the darkest periods.

The philosophies of mystic and alchemical import had no place in this disturbed western world. People found it hard to live. In religion there was western Catholicism, Arianism with Gnostic influences in Spain and North Africa, and the deeply philosophical and wise peace of the Byzantine church just to the east.

To the north and west the religion of Wotan and the Aesir had made a great advance, isolating the Celtic Christians from the mainstream of development. Yet the mystical thought of the old religions both of the Celts, as modified under the Church, and of the heathens, left a legacy of ideas about gold, dragons, and mystic fires, which was of importance in alchemical thought. One must always remember that western medieval culture had a mixed parentage. Much of the development of alchemy in its great days then becomes clearer. There was a historical reason for its visions taking the forms we see in the manuscripts which we use as illustrations.

For a century and a half the development of civilization retreated to its ancient homelands. The wonderful Empire of Byzantium embraced Greece, southern Italy, Asia Minor, Syria, Palestine, Egypt, and North Africa. It was Christian in a very special way because Constantine had been its real founder and because it had saved Christian Roman civilization from total destruction at the hands of the invading peoples. But within the Byzantine fold there were many flocks, some of them very strange. As usual the main areas of dissent from the official unity were Egypt and Syria. In Egypt the ancient beliefs of the people were echoed in folklore and in the everyday rituals of the Coptic church. Manichaean thought in Syria led to heresies which were suppressed firmly, but which persistently reappeared. In some way the Manichaeans seem to have profited by the irruption of the Hun armies. Their belief spread around the borders of the Byzantine Empire reaching France, and then spread along the eastern confines of the Hun dominions to form a powerful community in western China. There was a very wide stage now set for the dissemination of ideas which later crystal-lized in the work of the alchemists. There was nothing primitive in this background, from all angles the material was developed by teachers who had a philosophical training. The thoughts connected with the various heretical cults were reasoned thoughts. Often the premises were wildly inaccurate from our point of view, but in those days the knowledge of the material structure of the universe was lacking. There were the theological basic truths, and the Aristotelian conception of the Four Elements. From these a spiritual truth could be reached about the nature of the Creation, but the knowledge of the structure of the physical world was necessarily minimal. There was bound to be some clash between the theoreticians and experi-menters, and between both of them and the state Church. Because of this the development of alchemy was bound to be somewhat secret and clothed in all its public utterances with a veil of allusions which were never direct facts.

It might be well at this point to take a more leisured look at the state of alchemy and the nature of the material which we know was available in the early days of the Byzantine Empire. It is true that much of importance may have been lost, but the following works must have been considered of crucial importance because they have survived, through copies of copies, right down to the present day. First and most reliable was the text we quoted at the beginning of this book: *The Emerald Tablet.* It is clear that its attribution to Hermes Trismegistus cannot be clearly established, because the being behind the name of the Thrice Powerful was firstly a composite god having his roots in Ṭehuti the god of wisdom. It would be wise to assume that the text as we have it evolved in Alexandria from more ancient material of temple ritual. If we assumed that it came from a fairly wide background and was later condensed and used as a basic religious text by a smallish esoteric sect in Alexandria we should probably understand it better. The text is not explicitly alchemical and yet it contains a grouping of ideas which can be expressed very easily in alchemical terms. It is interesting to seek its origins, but most unlikely that we shall ever find the facts, and, indeed, it is unimportant now since in its evolved form it was the basic text from which most of the other things grew. It was the root of all formal alchemy for at least twenty centuries.

Another ambiguous but vitally important figure was Maria Prophetissa, said to be Miriam sister of Moses, but also called Maria the Jewess. Probably the real lady behind this name was also an Alexandrian experimenter. In alchemical thought she was often made into a fourth completing figure to a trio of male names. She was credited with many books and sayings, which were varied and expanded and even mixed with parts of the Christian liturgy. However, there can be no doubt that there really was a lady named Maria or Miriam who possessed a remarkable intellect. She was credited with the invention of a special form of still with three necks which could be fitted to the more ancient reflux apparatus and keep three types of distillate liquid in vases attached to it. The dome was likened to a woman's breast because of its shape, and because of the heated vapours liquefied within it to produce more delicate liquids; these however were drained away through the three tubes into flasks, and not through the nipple-like projection left on top where the glass blower's rod had been attached.

Mostly however we find that Maria Prophetissa is credited with a series of alchemical aphorisms which we shall meet with from time to time. They are quite clear to anyone who knows the general terminology used by alchemists, but their poetic nature led to further speculations of a mystical kind.

Other builders of apparatus which was the precursor of the still were Zosimus and Dioscorides. They were both concerned with the distillation of mercury and deposition of metals, though the work they performed led to the development of some interesting metal-eating acids. F. S. Taylor has shown that their work was really more connected with the production of metallic alloys than the increase of true gold in any way. It appears that the earliest alchemists had been interested in a kind of ritual chemistry in which the gilding of lower metals was a symbol of the changes in the human personality which came after initiation into the mystery.

There is a little evidence which tells of an altar and a priest who described visions of the soul's adventures in terms of the melting of ore and the purification and gilding of metals till one had become a shining golden spiritual being. The alchemical furnace on a small altar must have been a visual representation of the mystery. At the top one could see the movements and distillations of liquid and the deposition of mercury and its amalgamation with gold and repeated distillation to leave pure golden surfaces. The whole quadrature of the elements was apparent. Earth (stone or powered ore) was entered and Fire applied. Air rose in the form of gases and vapour, and Water of various kinds, like mercury and dilute acids, was distilled. For the initiates this was an object lesson of great significance. They had mysterious powers because the activity going on in the furnace and *kerotakis* on the altar produced wonderful results, which they hoped were also being reproduced in themselves. They must have been aware of the analogies of alchemy with life, and the actual construction of the human body. At this period there was a dawning consciousness of the reflection of sexual experience in the process, but it was probably as innocent and much less overt than the sexual side of most worship in the ancient world.

There is a total absence of information which would lead to the conclusion that the early alchemists were experimental scientists trying to discover new truths. They were trying simply to demonstrate the allegory of nature which had meant so much to the great adepts in past times. It is likely that as with the later alchemists they were oriented towards past times. The search was for the religion and magical power of the ancients. In that the studies led towards a higher state of being through contemplations of the work of God through the powers of nature, they probably did some good. And of course the very fact that the initiates were performing a ritual helped to heighten their emotions and so released many archetypal forms from their unconscious minds, which coloured the ideas they consciously held about the display of natural laws.

It has been suggested that the Perfected Sulphur used in the more famous of such religiously ecstatic experiments was really the sulphurous fumes produced from the distillation of eggs. This procedure would eventually produce vapours which could act as a superficial dye to metals. The observers were aware that the heat from the furnace provided a calcined mass from which arose white fumes which attacked the metal; these finally returned by convection to be re-heated until eventually the calcined ash glowed red, the metals becoming slightly oxydized on the surface showing a mystic rainbow iridescence. This iridescence is familiar to all who have seen a bowl of molten lead, but to the alchemists its appearance was like the peacock's tail which heralded the completion of the work. What work? None of the apparatus known to us would produce any practical result. However, some repetition of experiments in France in modern times suggests that under the special circumstances of repeated re-distillation with a sealed crystal vessel some unusual chemical effects may have occurred. The reasons for the devotion to a constantly repeated experiment by the earliest alchemists, however, must have been entirely empirical. They had no modern means of checking on the scientific products of their work.

Some products of alchemical distillation were obvious, and some were really projections from the minds of the initiates. The practical side of the art was merely a routine of ritual, but the spiritual side was extremely important. Professor C. G. Jung pointed out the significance of the world-serpent represented as a serpent eating its own tail. In the well known early picture from the papyrus in Leiden known as *The Gold-making of Cleopatra* which has a schematic drawing of the kind of distillation apparatus designed by Maria the Jewess, there is a symbolic picture of the serpent eating its own tail. This serpent is half light and half dark. It is similar in import to the Chinese symbol of Yin and Yang. There are also figures like the moon and four stars . . . Are they the stars of the four quarters of the year? Also in a roundel with a philosophical text in Greek there is a little drawing of the new moon, the crescent of the old moon and a symbol of gold, like a ray. So we must conclude that the philosophy even at that date, round about AD 250, included very important elements of time in the rituals. The text is important. As translated by F. Sherwood Taylor in *The Alchemists* it reads: 'One is the Serpent which has its poison according to two compositions, and One is All and through it is All, and by it is All, and if you have not All, All is Nothing.' This of course is related to the serpent Ouroboros which is labelled 'One is All'. We could not have a better picture or description of the

*The Lycurgus Cup, probably made in Italy in the fourth century* BC, *looks like green chalcedony outside but glows red when lit from inside*

necessity for the individual to recognize the inner unity of the conscious mind with the great unconscious which is partly the shadow side of ourselves. In its magical terms the picture is a statement of what Jung termed 'individuation'. It was the unity of the personality, in the knowledge of a deeper reality than most people could comprehend, which inspired the alchemists. Similarly another ritual inspired the Eleusinian initiates with the same unity of soul.

The early writer known to us only as Zosimus gives details of a series of visions which may indeed be manufactured, but which contain evidence of having derived from a true inspirational vision. The visionary saw an altar shaped like a bowl at the top of a stepped ascent. At three different stages he is shown a priestly person who is utterly destroyed before his eyes; each one of these stages describes the visionary's inner nature. It is as if different levels of the personality are being manifested and stripped away as one ascends towards the cauldron-altar of knowledge. (One notes the parallel with the Cauldron of Keridwen in Celtic mythology.) A priest is cut to pieces and before the remains are destroyed in the fire he vomits himself out as a manikin. A man of copper is destroyed and revives as a small man clothed in red. An old prophetic figure is taken and, white with age, is thrown into the cauldron. Finally the bearer of the Meridian of the Sun is himself dismembered and the visionary can then behold the mystery. This last is no doubt a time symbol, for only when time is in abeyance can mysteries which seem unreasonable reach a solution. The seer has ascended the seven steps of wisdom. This could be explained by some modern mathematicians as a picture of ascent into multi-dimensional existence at stages rising beyond our three-dimensional world. But for the alchemist this was all a poetic vision which held an inner truth about the world and the soul. It seems that the idea was also closely associated with the stage by stage development of the embryo from fertilization to birth; at least the document of the discussion between Cleopatra and the philosophers leads one to such a conclusion.

There is evidence enough here that, at the time of the creation of the Byzantine Empire, alchemical thought had reached a philosophical expression which hinted at a greater and mysterious past. In itself it was to be the foundation of a path of discovery which was ever seeking to return on itself and discover its own roots. It was strangely enough the equivalent of the serpent Ouroboros devouring its own tail.

For another century and a half the development of alchemy went on at the periphery of the Byzantine Empire. It is true that the state Church included many philosophical priests who were interested in the problems of

25

the relation between God and His Creation, but many paths led away from the orthodox opinions of the day. There is nothing to lead us to suppose that either Church or state could countenance the thought of an evolution in the human understanding of the Divine Mysteries. So the orthodox tended to play for safety and not to venture into fields of speculation. There can be little doubt that for the period this was the right attitude. The survivals of Gnostic thought are not to be seen as very serious philosophies, but rather as magical speculation. The ideas of the Arians in the west and the Manichaeans in the east brought confusion to the teachers of simple doctrine, so persecutions were unleashed and the unorthodox found no peace. That is why the alchemical tradition lingered only in border areas which were later to be overrun by the Saracens. The Byzantine writers on alchemy who we know were Easterners on the borders of Persia, were not people near the court. If there was a western European tradition it was to be submerged under the Islamic armies. If that tradition emerged later in Islamic Spain we have no certain means of knowing since the great thinkers of Islam were echoing alchemical teachings which arose in Syria, Persia and Arabia. No doubt there was a tradition alive in Egypt, but the factions of Alexandria and the constant turmoil of that city under the Byzantines made any philosophy difficult to develop. The Coptic Church was not regarded as part of the true Byzantine tradition and was pushed more and more to the borders. Byzantine Egypt was rich in all the arts and technologies, but no longer a centre of peaceful development of learning.

Then, to complete the blackening and decay of the philosophy of alchemy came the Arab invasion, and the miraculous conquests of Islam. The Prophet was not a man without learning, neither were his major supporters, but there was an emotional current of what we should call Puritanism within the first founders of the Islamic Empire. The knowledge of God as revealed to the Prophet through the Koran was the sufficient knowledge of all things. The recital of the simple Islamic declaration of faith carried the believer's soul to Paradise, the more so if it was offered to Allah on the field of mortal struggle for the advance of the faith. In this spirit the great library of Alexandria was swept over and utterly disrupted. It is true that many of the warriors were simple tribesmen obeying their family chiefs, having no wish but to conquer and die; but many another of the Arabs thought quite sincerely that the books scattered and burnt were but heathen mouthings of no relevance to a simple revealed faith. One can appreciate the attitude of the Arab army; yet the destruction and dispersal of the Alexandrian library was a disaster for the continuity of human civilization.

The period of the holy wars which spread Islam from Persia to Morocco was the ending of an era. The classical world foundered not as a whole, but as a series of small surviving regions in a rapidly evolving Byzantine cultural hegemony. The new spirit was alive in the Eastern Empire before the Islamic conquests. What the Mediterranean civilized world was facing was not really barbarism or real darkness, but a division into three regions, each concerned with its religious exclusiveness. Islamic, Frankish, and Byzantine civilizations were each dependent on religious teachings for their very roots. The men of learning centred around the mosque and the church. The most vital of the regions, the West, was especially alive because of the magnitude of the disasters which had broken the old Empire to fragments. New peoples with new ideas had swept into the area of civilization. But in Byzantium and in the centres of the Arab world traditional learning was most acceptable. Rich developments were to take place, but they were to come mostly from an extension of formal religious philosophy. The more experimental thought was to come from the borderlands. In particular the traditions of alchemical philosophy were to develop again from the teaching preserved by Nestorians, Monophysites, and Manichees in Persia, Syria and Iraq.

In the seventh and eighth centuries the apparent fall into darkness was completed. The old learning must have seemed lost irretrievably to most thinking people, and its remains were just the black ash of burned manuscripts drifting in the winds at Alexandria.

# 3

# aqua ardens

Historically it was the function of the Arab philosophers to recreate the alchemical philosophy. They took the ancient confusions, repeated traditional experiments and developed a new way of scientific appreciation which lifted the ancient mystery religion to a new state of a rational experiment with more material aims. In doing this they approached a coherent system, and this evolved in time into the modern scientific approach to chemistry. Nevertheless the Arabs retained much mysticism in their approach to the alchemical process. It was still linked with the double approach of making gold and of revealing a doctrine which could bring enlightenment to the soul. The eastern boundaries of the Byzantine Empire were the homes of the more important heresies wherein the thoughts about the link between the powers of man and God were very active. As Persia, Syria and Iraq became part of the Caliphate, and their learning developed under the new regime, it is not strange that that much Manichaean, and Nestorian thought including alchemy was assimilated. Thus the way was prepared for a school of Islamic thought which went far beyond the simple faith of the conquest period. It later crystallized as Sufi teaching, and the Isma'ili sect became involved.

The first important name in Arab alchemy is that of Prince Khalid, a noble Arabian who was the younger brother of the Caliph, Muawiya II. He is known to have been living in Damascus from about 660 to 704; in the period when the Muslim armies were held up in North Africa by Berber resistance before they captured the Visigothic kingdoms of Spain. Khalid was the reputed author of some thousands of verses of poetry on alchemical themes, but most of them are apocryphal. He is said to have learned the art from an Alexandrian Christian, Morienus, who had been a pupil of the famous alchemist Zosimus. Morienus is said to have actually transmuted base metal to gold before Khalid, but had to escape into exile because at that time the Prince accused the Alexandrians of fraud. However, there was a later meeting which seems to have impressed Prince Khalid more favourably and inspired his study on the subject. In the general confusion of this period of history, even the specialists are uncertain how much of the development of Islamic alchemy is faithfully reported in context with its true date. It is abundantly clear that the famous names were credited with works actually written by later members of their school of philosophy. No doubt future studies will bring much more material to light, but also the poetic tendency in Islamic literature, which is evident in such works as the *Arabian Nights' Entertainments*, also intruded into works concerned with medicine and alchemy. It is as if one amalgamated a text book on physics with a volume of science fiction. One is led into many unclear conclusions and unbelievable accounts are often the only signposts.

However, not long after Khalid, we come to one of the best documented of all Arab writers, Jabir ibn Hayyan. His life extended from about 722 to 815. His father, Hayyan, was born in the city of Kufa on the Euphrates, originally the home of a group of marsh-dwelling peoples who had been resettled in a new city by Caliph Omar nearly two centuries earlier. He was an expert in medicinal drugs and also a politician of note who was involved in the plotting to overthrow the Ummayad family and replace them by the Abbassid line of caliphs. However, during his travels he stayed in the Persian town of Tus, and there it appears that Jabir was born. Later on Hayyan was seized and killed at the instigation of the last of the Ummayad caliphs, and Jabir as a boy was sent to relatives in Arabia for an education in classical Arabic and mathematics. He followed his father's studies in medicine, and also developed great learning in the properties of materials because he had an original mind and was willing to experiment. Consequently he was brought into contact with books and ideas about alchemy. He returned to live in Kufa and became noted as a philosopher and alchemist.

Much to his credit, Jabir was a member of the Sufi movement, seeking wisdom by meditation and exercises of the mind which led to ecstatic union with the mind of God. The philosophy of the Sufi led to a puritan way of life as a protest against luxury and moral confusion in the courts of the nobles. They found in their studies many ideas which derived from Greek Neo-platonism, and so added a wider outlook in the world of reasoned thought to that of their more orthodox contemporaries.

The Sufi path brought Jabir into contact with manuscripts deriving from Syria which contained much of the alchemical knowledge of the earlier world. It was a stepping stone for his practical approach to the mysteries of nature; and also an incentive for his mind to take the mystical flight into a world of symbolic numbers and significant letters. The origins of this line of thought were at once Greek and Egyptian. The Greeks had developed the idea of special meanings to be given to each numeral irrespective of its simple meaning as number. The Egyptian contribution was the concept of the magical value of the written word and of the letters themselves as powerful magic because they were uttered by Ṭehuti the god of wisdom. In fact Jabir in his own life experienced the impact of all the factors which had built up alchemy before his time, and he was able to organize those ideas through his form of Sufi mystic experience. It is not surprising that in his hands alchemy developed a new form which, although based on the older material, was more organized and more experimentally minded.

In later times Jabir came to be considered in western Europe as one of the Fathers of Alchemy and was known as the Arabian Geber. In more recent times, alas, his name was used in derision of mystic language which was incomprehensible to the masses, hence the corruption 'gibberish'. But in his own day Jabir had a tiny link with western Europe, perhaps even through his books, since he was the court alchemist to the great Haroun er Rashid who exchanged gifts of great value with his contemporary, the Frankish Emperor Charlemagne.

Jabir's advancement came through his close friendship with the Barmecide family who were for a long time the advisers to the caliph. It was through Ja'far al Sadiq that he received much of his learning and from another Ja'far the Barmecide his introduction to Haroun er Rashid himself. For the caliph he wrote a *Book of Venus*, describing his alchemical experiments in poetic form.

It is said that Jabir also exerted his influence to increase allowances for the purchase and translation of Greek books from the Eastern Empire at Byzantium. This brought him a wealth of information in many sciences in which he was interested, and made him one of the most truly learned men of his age. However, he eventually retired to Kufa to continue his researches and studies in seclusion. This was in 803, when the caliph, tired of the over-weening pride of his Barmecide advisers, decided to dismiss the lot. With them went his alchemist. However, it is clear that Jabir was not a great sufferer through enforced retirement. He was already nearly eighty years of age and a greatly respected writer and scholar. The story goes that two centuries after his death some builders making a new house in Kufa came upon the ruins of his laboratory and, although nothing else was found, neither vessels nor powders of any kind, in a corner of a room they found a mortar for grinding fine powders, and it was made of pure gold. This may be apocryphal, but the thought is in line with alchemical understanding . . . the brass which becomes gold, the treasure neglected in the dust at one's feet.

Of the reputed work of Jabir too much remains. His name was so revered that many later works on medicine and alchemy were ascribed to him by writers who saw a unity of intent in all works of Sufi philosophy on alchemy. Later works of the Isma'ili sect (which was founded a generation after the death of Jabir) become so involved with his writings that they were usually ascribed to his authorship. However, this shows that the work of Jabir was so highly respected that it was the foundation for almost all later thought about alchemy in the Islamic world. It was similarly a tenet among western alchemists that Geber was the great re-founder of the ancient art subsequent to the fall of Roman imperial power.

There were real scientific advances made through Jabir's work. He is credited with the preparation of nitric acid, of various rare salts, and with experiments in the distillation of many natural substances. This was all part of his work in the classification of the materials in the world of nature. His medical knowledge was used in the preparation of elixirs which are reputed to have had almost miraculous effects. His design of apparatus led to the development of the still in a form which we know today. This was a great advance on the more primitive *kerotakis*, and involved the use of the alembic to distribute the products of distillation into receiving flasks.

The theoretical basis of much of the experimental work was not reasonable from our point of view, and it cannot be fully understood by the modern mind. The reason is that it was based on non-material considerations. A 'magic square' is constructed with five in the centre, using only digits, and in such a way that each line adds up to $5 \times 3 = 15$:

|   |   |   |
|---|---|---|
| 4 | 9 | 2 |
| 3 | 5 | 7 |
| 8 | 1 | 6 |

From this one separates the square indicated leaving a set-square or gnomon of the remaining figures.

We then total them, obtaining 17 and 28. These are numbers which Jabir assumes, in accordance with Sufi philosophy, to be natural numbers concerned in all the movements and combinations of natural things. Then one takes the 28 letters of the Arabic alphabet. These letters are letters of power, and to Jabir they must be Arabic since that was the alphabet in which the Koran was written. All matter is to be classified in accordance with these letters distributed in numerical variations of the natural qualities, heat, cold, dryness and moistness. (Fire, Air, Earth and Water). By dividing up the Arabic name for a substance and ascribing numerical values to each letter we arrive at a numeral value expressing its composition in terms of the four Aristotelian elements. This is in effect all 'gibberish'. Yet when one looks at the complex elements there is evidence that it all has a philosophical basis. It describes thoughts about the natural world and has nothing to do with such hard facts as atomic weights and valencies. One should look at the 'Magic Square' above and begin to think of the meaning of the numbers in one's own mind. Then one can begin to comprehend Jabir's thought, as a kind of philosophy, and nothing like what we recognize as a science today. Actually we are back once again to the psychological basis of thought where meanings are projected upon numbers. In Jabir's case it was complicated by the Arabic system of weights and measures which was apparently as irrational as the Avoirdupois system.

However, Jabir advocated the study of the numerical relations in his system between various substances. One had to determine how these differed from gold. Then an elixir was to be prepared which would redress the balance, and by the right method of combination bring about the change. By this method any one substance could be transmuted into any other. This was an utterly irrational idea which, in another form, has appeared really scientifically in our present knowledge of the inner structure of the atom. Jabir was working on non-rational mathematical constructions and the modern scientist is working with carefully checked studies of the qualities of actual 'particles' which constitute the material universe.

Of course the alchemical constitution of a material form did not always yield a useful number and so the theory grew up that the outward form of a metal should have one name and the inner, real quality should have another; this method would lead to the correct mathematical formula for transmutation. Thus we have the germ of the alchemists' idea that the important substances of their art were not the same as those seen by the common people. The differentiation between philosophic gold and vulgar gold is really the equivalent of Jabir's idea of the outer and inner nature of the metals.

Be that as it may, the Arabs of the caliphate had a firm belief in alchemy, and Jabir as well as many other wise and elderly philosophers are described as having found the wonderful powders, the red and the white powder which could transmute metals into gold in different degrees of richness.

It was probably some time after Jabir's death that the Greek manuscripts in which he had taken so great an interest were sorted and re-edited in the form of a discussion of the Greek alchemists and their forerunners the philosophic Platonists, generally fitting into the Sufi mould. It was later re-translated in Europe as the famous *Turba Philosophorum*. Thus again an Arab collection preserved some of the most important early alchemical ideas for the future when civilization should have returned to the West.

Western Europe was in some confusion over the whole period of Arab alchemical discovery. The bright hopes of the Empire of Charlemagne were clouded and distorted by his incapable successors. However, his drive for the education of the clergy had important results. Learning once more became important. The scholars who brought new life to the West found help in the study of secular Latin literature, and in an occasional period of study in Spain which, under the Arabs, was the centre of culture and learning of the whole of the West. The wars and struggles between dynasts descended from Odin, and now become Christians, kept Europe from any fast advance in learning, but within it all the occasional genius arose.

One of the most brilliant of Europeans near the end of the Dark Ages was Bishop Gerbert of Aurillac, who made the first mechanical clock, in order to awaken his monks for night vigils by the ringing of a bell at the appropriate time. He made studies of the natural sciences so that, even though he became Pope Saint Sylvester II, he acquired a reputation for being a magician. He had travelled to Cordoba in Spain to study mathematics, and also collected books of many kinds, possibly, but not certainly, including Arab works on the natural world and alchemy. In later times there was some confusion between Geber the Arabian and Gerbert the philosopher, but Gerbert was recognized by later alchemists as one of themselves. We may conclude that he had heard of and probably made some study of the other Geber: Jabir ibn Hayyan. He was in Cordoba when Maslama ibn Ahmad was teaching alchemical doctrine and mathematics in Madrid, and Muhammad ibn Umail was working on his alchemical poems and studies which entered the world of European alchemy in translation only two centuries later. In a small way, through the contacts between intellectual individuals, the link between the Islamic and Christian alchemists was taking shape, and, of course, uniting the future with the pre-Islamic past of the alchemical art.

Another contemporary of Pope St Sylvester II was the great physician and scientist, Abu Ali ibn Sina (Avicenna), who was born near Bokhara in 980 and died about 1037. He was a brilliant youth, seeking knowledge of all kinds and studying and experimenting on his own account when he found his teachers could go no further. When he was sixteen he was already consulted as an authority on medicine. He seems to have studied all the works available on alchemy, and used many of the processes to discover new compounds and to distil medicines. However, he came to the conclusion that alchemy was not a science and that the evidence for the actual trans-mutation of metals into gold was not reliable. Avicenna followed Jabir in believing that all metals were constituted of varying proportions of mercury and sulphur. His view was almost that of the Alexandrian metallurgists, since he saw alchemy as a means of altering the external aspects of metals only, by reddening white metals to make them stimulate gold and whitening red metals to give the appearance of silver. This attack on alchemy was challenged by other authorities who pointed out that he had quoted works by Jabir and his later successor, Al Razi, and yet disagreed about the final conclusions. There was much controversy, and neither supporters nor denigrators of alchemy were deterred at all by the opinion of the great scientist.

In the ensuing three centuries there were few really great alchemists in the Islamic world. Their work was not original, but largely consisted of combinations of previous ideas taken from the great masters of the past. It is amply evident that the great days of Islamic alchemy were coming to an end, and that as in China the original ideas of 'chemical' alchemy were to be absorbed into a framework of religious meditation rather than the material development of a metallurgical chemistry. The pathway was to lead to European investigators, who were to take the Arabic knowledge and try to make a pragmatic procedure of alchemy in which, at first, the philosophical side was little different from the ideas of the Arabs.

We may go right back to the advice which the Alexandrian, Morienus, is said to have given Prince Khalid:

God commands his carefully chosen servants that they seek out this Divine and Holy science that they keep it to themselves hidden carefully from the generality of men. This knowledge takes its possessor away from the suffering of this world and leads him to the knowledge of future blessing. . . . The gateway to peace is exceedingly narrow and no one may enter except through the agony of his own soul.

Yet all through the Islamic world alchemical studies continued and laboratories were made for the study of this strange ritual aiming as much at purification of the soul as the transmutation of base metal to gold. Much of the ancient knowledge remained in Morocco until modern times, and it may be that this knowledge has influenced modern experiments in France.

The Arab contribution to alchemy was great. It at once conserved the ideas of antiquity and expanded them through the development of new apparatus and new lines of philosophic thought. The invention of nitric acid alone would have justified the title of this chapter, but the Islamic regimen of thought drew together the old material wherever it was available and extracted many good things from it. They arrived at new unity which was understood by all philosophically minded men from the borders of India to the Spanish plateau by the time that the Europeans had begun their slow climb back to the world of knowledge and scientific discussion.

# 4

# SUBLIMATION

In the tenth and eleventh centuries there was constant small-scale inter-
change of ideas between the western Europeans and the Islamic nations.
Internal political divisions were as important as the clash between the
Church and Islam. The Arabs, remembering vaguely the nationality of
Charles Martel and Charlemagne, called all the Westerners Franks, and did
not admire them the more for it. It probably suggested a race of uncultured
and ferocious barbarians of whom a few individuals attained some material
power and importance, and still fewer reached the point where they were
worthy to study in Arab schools in Spain and Sicily. But the Europeans
were themselves disunited. Struggles for power between the older established kingdoms and the newly-formed northern nations were keeping
their lands in a turmoil. This mingling of cultural waves brought a renewal
of ancient ideas from the old northern heathendom. These were expressed
in art which broke away from the formal bond of permitted ideas of almost
Byzantine strictness. The carvers, jewellers and illustrators discovered a
world of pictorial excitement, and used it to illustrate the teaching of their
church.

In the freedom of their art-work the western Europeans had something
which was available only in a restricted form to the Islamic writers. From
time to time the prohibition of the representation of the things of the
natural world was enforced strictly, and at other times it still had a great
influence on what could be approved in art. Thus the Islamic alchemist
was usually restricted to a world of words and symbols within which his
thoughts had to be expressed. On the other hand, the way was open for the
Europeans to escape into another method of expression. At first the
possibilities of pictorial expression may have inhibited the need of scholars
for a system of practical philosophy to give them a spiritual release, but later,
as the western Europeans acquired a deeper education they were to find that
their studies of alchemy, learned from the Arabs, were to be greatly enriched

36

by their pictorial traditions. A new channel of release for the visions derived from the alchemical discipline was created. It is this, much more than the consciously balanced phrases and deliberately concealing words, which makes alchemy live for us.

An interesting feature of the western European cultures was the persistence of ancient folk-lore which had roots in both Celtic and Norse heathendom. Charlemagne had a collection of ancient Saxon and Frankish poems and songs which his foolish son destroyed after his death. But many other fragments of old mythology remained, particularly the later compilation of Norse legend made by Snorri Sturlasson in Iceland, and the Celtic lore preserved in the Mabinogion. We find this literature contains obscure references to ideas of the suffering hero who is transmuted by his pains. Odin hanging on the sacred ash tree Yggdrasil is almost like the metal on the little tray of an early *kerotakis*. Below is the well of wisdom and also the fumes of Nifelheim, above is the dew and the birds. The secret knowledge acquired by the god comes from a universe pictured as a great reflex of forces strikingly like the alchemical demonstration of distillation and deposition of metals. The thoughts of the dragon guarding the treasure, and the world-serpent foreshadowed the ideas which have a rich pictorial flowering in the alchemical books.

In the Celtic field we have many links with the deities associated with the moon and the varying aspects of the sun. However, the great wonder of the Celtic Druids was the iridescent Serpent's Egg, a rainbow-like ball which contained all wisdom. There was also the Cauldron of Keridwen which contained the elixir of life and the draught of enlightenment, for those who dare approach it . . . for this cauldron was ancestor to the idea of the Holy Grail which might only be seen by the pure in heart.

That the alchemists included such pictorial images and ancient traditions in their works was not a direct copying by antiquarians but an independent discovery of archetypal myths within their own being, crystallized by their contemporary folk tradition, probably heard in childhood. In Germany too there was the development of the Baldur myth with its thoughts of opposed dark and light and the funeral pyre and a higher world of the gods to which the hero passed.

We could not expect their knowledge of human life to allow the alchemists to become simply scientific recorders of fact. The tradition had always been aimed at showing the road to perfection, and the surrounding world of tradition gave a ready made *mythos* for them to develop from their own souls.

Once pictorial imagery had entered alchemy it was set on a course of advancement which made it almost like a religion. In fact it was returning to its original aspects, and in the process it would shed its skin of strictly chemical knowledge and become altogether philosophical. Yet the chemical knowledge which it passed on to others was in due course to prove the clue to another alchemy – that of infra-atomic structures.

However, in the tenth and eleventh centuries the world of books and teaching was small, and the mental atmosphere was tense. The millennium was there, and change was expected. The dangers of everyday life in the monasteries and towns were great in unsettled times, and people saw visions and dreamed wonders. Thus, because of artistic tradition, mythological echoes, and the release of archetypes from the inner mind of the artists and seers, we find many things which appear to be alchemical without actually having a direct contact with that specially Hermetic art.

In spite of the increasing religious tension between Islamic and Christian communities there was always a steady flow of learned pilgrims from the great centres of religious learning in Christendom who had felt the need to seek learning in the Islamic universities. They were not only seeking for the natural sciences; little by little they discovered that further works by the scholars of ancient times, the Romans and Greeks, were available in Arabic versions. Sometimes a few precious manuscripts of the fourth and fifth centuries survived for study.

In those centuries many foundations were laid for the development of European civilization by men who are mostly not even names to us. They could not have foreseen that their limited collaboration would lead to important international and inter-confessional toleration and understanding. They saw the acquisition of learning as a necessity for studying their own religion and winning its supremacy in the future. The Crusades were developing phenomena, yet religious scholars, the only scientists of those days, still met and disputed in peace within the Islamic cities.

In his work *Psychology and Alchemy*, C.G.Jung quotes from *Theatrum Chemicum*, Vol. V a *Liber Platonis quartorum* which belongs in origin to the tenth century:

The Philosopher in the Book of Dialogues said: 'I walked round the Three Heavens, namely the heaven of composite natures, the heaven of discriminated natures and the heaven of the soul. But when I wished to walk round the heaven of intelligence, the soul said unto me: "That is no way for thee", then nature attracted me, and I was attracted.' The philosopher did not come to this conclusion in order to give this science a name, but because he wished to make sure that his words would not fail to reveal the power which liberates the creature. His purpose was to make us recognize the lower process in this kind of work by the Higher.

This not only provides a wonderful text for a discussion, but it points out that to the alchemist, even as late as the seventeenth century, the mystery was part of the conformity between the microcosm and the macrocosm – the lower material process showed the higher. Nevertheless, at the higher levels of the three heavens, which are also like alchemical processes, the composite natures moving through refining to the discriminated nature, observed by the soul (the inner personality equivalent to the unconscious); the observer is warned not to follow intelligence. It is implied that an emotional involvement, a mutual attraction between the philosopher and nature is the real essential in the process. We are right back with the traditions of the earliest alchemists who observed the process as a ritual in which the chemical changes were like the changes in the soul of the initiate. However, the insistence upon the observation of nature must have had a great appeal to the European mind in the period around the millennium. It was a case of the wonders of nature showing the mysteries of the universe. Quite naturally it was felt that one who had witnessed this sublime exposition of the unity of nature, where the metals and chemicals were all paralleled with the distant planets and stars, must become an ennobled person. But not everybody could profit from the experience. It needed the purified soul and the clear mind of the philosopher to approach the alchemical mystery.

We can now understand the kind of personality which was necessary for an alchemist. The mind must be devoted to the pursuit of understanding, through a realization that on every level in nature there is a symbolic answer to the ultimate problems of existence. The search for the secret of matter, its purification and transformation to gold, must be accompanied by a search for the secret of the planets and stars, and also a search within oneself. The result would be a comprehension of the nature of God and of His work of Creation. While such a system of thought was easily possible for a Sufi scholar, very few western Europeans could attain to that stage in the millennial period. Great souls meditated and found a path to heaven through their faith, and clear minds disputed theology and law; but there were few who could grasp the idea of the importance of studying the material world as a clue to a wider understanding than that revealed in the Scriptures. In fact they must have been regarded as faintly heretical, whether Sufi or Christian.

In the succeeding eleventh and twelfth centuries there was a great awakening in Europe. In particular the vigorous Normans, only recently brought into the sphere of Christianity, showed the most remarkable capacity for learning as well as ruling. Their fantastic successes in southern Italy, first with the conquest of Apulia and later of Sicily brought them into contact with new ways of life. They enjoyed luxuries undreamed of by their grandparents, saw wonders of the arts all around them, and then found their subjects had a long tradition of the type of knowledge which could bring them a new kind of civilized status. These subject people included many Mohammedans, some of them wise doctors and others philosophers. They accepted the domination of the Normans and mostly became Christians, but they had much to give in the way of philosophy to the churchmen who were supported liberally by the Norman nobility. Sicily was no longer ruled by the Tunisians, it was once more part of Europe and new influences were assimilated, including something of alchemical knowledge.

Meanwhile the Islamic state was no longer unified. Egypt was separated from the caliphate because of the support its rulers gave to the Shiiah sect in Islam, the rulers of the Maghrib were mostly independent, while in Spain there was tension and sometimes bloodshed between Arab and Berber factions among the rulers. However, in Spain the great teaching centres, especially at Cordoba, were the preservers of the mainstream of Islamic philosophy in the west. It was because of the division of the Islamic states that the capture of Sicily by the Normans, and of Corsica by the Italians did little to upset the tolerant relations between the scholars of both religions in the West.

In the East another problem arose. Byzantium was threatened, the remaining Syrian provinces of the Empire were torn away and the provinces of Asia Minor were under direct assault from the Seljuk Turks. The Seljuk advance also weakened the caliphate, since they had cut off a great part of Persia, and then proceeded eventually to take over the regions of Iraq and Syria. Eventually the caliphate became Turkish. However, the Turkish advance into Asia Minor had to be repelled, and the Emperor appealed for help from western Christendom. This unleashed the unpleasant First Crusade which led to insult of the Emperor and the robbing of Byzantine wealth, although it did secure a coastal strip of Asia Minor to Byzantium for a while. The Crusaders went south, and fought on their own against the already weakened Arab forces. They established a Norman kingdom of Jerusalem.

Out of this almost unbelievable turmoil came important human contacts for the remaining Byzantine alchemists. The kingdom of Jerusalem had contacts, often surprisingly peaceful, with leading Arab thinkers, disturbed at the advances of the Turks. Manichaean heretics returned to the Byzantine borderlands and their ideas spread more widely again; the ancient knowledge kept in Byzantine libraries began to be opened to the West. Once more the world seemed to have been turned over and the political and social

*A section of the first* Ripley Scrowle, *painted in Lübeck in 1588; it shows the seven processes of the alchemist*

structure of Europe changed. In the quiet moments learning spread, and the progress of the renaissance of learning in the West advanced apace. With it went alchemical studies which were quite suddenly less dependent upon Cordoba. The Franks were establishing their own centres of learning.

In Apulia the Normans were learning from the schools of medicine in Sicily. In Spain the scholars sent from the churches in France and Britain were learning Arabic in order to translate works of philosophy into Latin. In Byzantium older philosophical texts were being re-studied, and made available to the few of the western barbarians who bothered to enquire of the more ancient learning. Some of them also began to learn Greek, with a view to gathering knowledge into the fold of Latin teaching.

The first fruit of the Latinization of alchemy was *The Book of the Composition of Alchemy* completed on 11 February 1144 by Robert of Chester. This work appeared at the time of a great revival of the intellectual life in the west of Europe. This was the age of wise men, and Robert was no exception; he was Abbot of Pamplona in Christian Spain, a writer on algebra, astronomy and mathematics. For him the alchemical work was an extension of the natural sciences. His intellectual outlook was probably influenced by the ideas of Abelard who had died in 1142. Abelard had stood, in his idiosyncratic way, for the use of reason as a means of enriching faith. This concept was opposed by St Bernard and ultimately condemned, but Abelard's near-deathbed reconciliation with the official Churchmen must have given his ideas a better chance to spread. Robert of Chester certainly developed the natural sciences by bringing his Arabic material to the notice of the scholars of Europe; but in so doing he introduced an important cross-current in alchemy which was bound to turn towards science and eventually separate into scientific chemistry, and a form of transcendentalism.

Each of the two attitudes of mind was right, but for centuries they could not combine. Alchemy was doomed from the beginning of its introduction to the western Europeans; but through the centuries of exasperating experiment and disappointment many fascinating human personalities passed through the laboratories. At this early stage the great teachers were churchmen of wide scholarship, and they disagreed on the fundamental of the scientific side of alchemy. Could gold be produced by alchemical means or not? Albertus Magnus followed the Arabian scholar Avicenna in accepting that the alchemical process would result in superficial colouring or plating of metals; St Thomas Aquinas was more in accord with the modern scientific attitude that, given the proper knowledge, the structure of matter could be refined and changed ... though he did not of course have any inkling of inter-atomic physics.

We may take it that these great men to whom the knowledge of all the science of their day was open, considered alchemy to be but a small part of natural science. Neither had been so impressed that he considered it to be in more than an experimental stage. Already a considerable number of translations from the Arabic were available to them. They were looking at them from a strictly orthodox angle, and had not been influenced by the underlying philosophical ideas about alchemy as a figure of the structure of the universe which should unite man with the whole of creation. It must be remembered that they were teachers in a religious and social setting which was authoritarian in the extreme. Their work was accomplished in the period of the ghastly crusade against the Albigenses; and so any unorthodox views would have been edited out of their thought. Alchemical speculation had in its origins many contacts with the ideas of the various groups whose philosophy developed towards Albigensian thought. It may be that the crusade was really inverted and repressed eroticism turned to violence against the less repressed, but the depth of feeling which resulted in atrocities of that magnitude must have coloured all orthodox thought of the time. It effectively repressed the linked ideas which later reappeared in the thoughts about the mystic rose and the idea of the male-female link through the *Soror Mystica* of later alchemical work.

Later alchemists in Europe ascribed many utterly apocryphal works to the great names of the past such as Albertus Magnus and Thomas Aquinas. This simply means that the philosophers were so greatly respected that their names were used to give authority, almost like good-luck charms. The fact was that Europe's first scientists were not alchemists, but were interested in that subject among much other work.

Whether the Knights Templars were ever involved directly in alchemy is very doubtful, but they had certainly imbibed many philosophical ideas from the Arab scientists. Nevertheless they found it necessary to conceal their heterodox ideas within the walls of their fortresses. Even when they were dissolved under the pressure exerted by the French king, Philippe le Bel, one finds no clear evidence of alchemy. However, the general picture makes one aware of an undercurrent of Sufi thought in their beliefs. Thus, at the dissolution of the order many socially important men, with minds already fit for the study of alchemy, were in Europe. First we must mention Friar Bacon, and Arnold of Villanova. They were both working at their best a generation after the destruction of the Albigenses. Both were orthodox churchmen, yet both were eccentric to such a degree that their work led them into conflict with the ecclesiastical authorities and landed them in prison more than once.

Of Roger Bacon (1214–92) much imaginary lore has been recounted. He studied philosophy and lectured in the University of Paris, where he became a Franciscan in 1247, and later lectured and taught at Oxford. He was deeply interested in mathematics and astronomy, and his fascination with the chemistry of the time, in which all metals were still regarded as combinations of mercury and sulphur, led him to a series of careful experimental works. His reasoning divided alchemy into two parts, one of which was purely experimental. Its aim was to perfect the knowledge of how to make the great medicines and elixirs, and how to purify metals to the point where they were true gold. The other part of the study was comparative and descriptive and, although Bacon called it speculative, it was the germ of chemical science as we know it.

Bacon conducted his researches amid a storm of polemics; having thoroughly upset his Superiors in the Order by his insistence on his superior knowledge he was imprisoned for fourteen years, and released only in the year before his death. He was really seeking knowledge rather than skill in magic, and in the process he found that he was obliged to study alchemy far more deeply than his predecessors. He sought knowledge of the material world in order to discover the inner links between metals which would make transmutation possible, thinking that it was a perfectly straightforward process, though one demanding much patience and skill. He does not show any trace of the heretical idea that through the ritual of the alchemical process one might enlighten the soul.

Arnold of Villanova (1235–1311) was more of a visionary in his scientific work, and although he did not have intimations of the future of science like those attributed to Friar Bacon, he was closely linked with a mystical approach to alchemy. His periods of imprisonment were really caused by political disputes about his relationship with the hierarchy of the Church. Like Bacon, his personal attacks on authoritarianism caused most of his troubles. However, apart from three years of what amounted to house arrest in Paris he was free to travel and teach quite freely. Arnold was apparently the first to describe alchemy as 'The Rosary of the Philosophers'. The term was used in many different ways in later centuries, but to Arnold it is likely that the term implied careful repetition in ascending series of experiments with interludes for meditation and prayer. It was certainly not just a series of actions on matter in a laboratory. He advocated the use of talismans with symbols on them as a means of aiding one in the path of life, but he emphasized that such objects were not magical and their efficacy demanded a reciprocal effort from the user. They were useful only to the pure in heart and mind. He was enunciating again the ancient principle that the work of the alchemist is to be taken as a unity of the experiment and the person making it. The alchemist must himself be a purified vessel prepared for the work just as the vessels he used in the experiments. In the life and passion of Christ he found a theological parallel to his rhythm of work. He also used scientific numerical ratios in preparing his material, though they have little meaning to the scientist of today. They sound very like the semi-magical numbers used in Arabic alchemy. He expects to see the regular colour changes and the beautiful colours of the Peacock's Tail, and then the formation of the already famous red powder. This powder from this time forward is the equivalent of the Philosopher's Stone. It must be treated with great care, and then very precisely added to mercury in order to make gold. There are stories of terrifying explosions in alchemical laboratories which suggest that the red powder in some cases was really fulminate of Mercury $Hg (ONC)_2$. The legend tells us that Friar Bungay and Friar Bacon blew themselves up at Oxford and flew off in the claws of the devil, but this is all apocryphal. No suggestion that Arnold of Villanova was taken away in a thunderclap of flame survives. However, he was undoubtedly a practising alchemist. He died peacefully at sea, not long after meeting Raymond Lully, at the age of seventy-six.

Alchemy was now established in the outward pattern which it held ever afterwards in Europe. Its spiritual content was already less important than in the days when the laboratory experiment was simply a demonstration of the mystery of the soul. It was now much more magical in feeling, and also much more scientific in its attitude to experimental advance. New chemical compounds were being studied as a part of natural science, new ideas from ancient myths were developing among the educated Europeans of the early fourteenth century. The renaissance was well under way. It is seen in a new naturalism in art, in a new attitude of mind which favoured scientific discipline in study, and in a willingness to accept new ideas. Many of these last must have been disseminated when the Templars were dissolved in 1312.

# 5

# condensation

The fourteenth century saw new tendencies in alchemy. It was widely discussed, the number of practitioners increased vastly, and it attracted official attention. Often the official attitude was stern, even if it were only to protect the wealthy citizens from the impositions of numbers of cheats and confidence tricksters who were involved in the new developments. This all became possible through the stabilization of European society. The feudal system had developed to its most efficient levels, and although war was endemic throughout the nations of western Europe, there was a general rise in cultural levels. Better organization of life, better trade and, above all, better education made it possible for knowledge to spread. The age was becoming deeply romantic, and developed the charming rituals of chivalry.

Among the alchemists the name of Raymond Lully has long been celebrated. He was a Catalan nobleman of a mystical temperament. His wild youth was followed by a serene philosophical Christianity. Raymond intended to spread religion among the infidels by direct argument and wise discussion. He travelled widely, and it is noteworthy that in eastern Europe and parts of Asia Minor he was able to make contacts among some of the heretical groups of Christians who had apparently returned within the failing framework of the Byzantine Empire. He finally tried direct missionary work in North Africa, but was rewarded by being stoned to death. His many writings on philosophy and religion include some of the great masterpieces of the Catalan language. But nowhere does he advocate alchemy. It appears that his wisdom, and method of thought, as well as his travels in strange places gave him a fantastic reputation. This included the tale that he transmuted a score of tons of brass and copper into gold for King Edward of England, when working with an 'Abbot Cremer' of Westminster. Since there is no trace of any Abbot Cremer, nor of any visit of the great teacher Raymond Lully to this country one must assume that it is all part of an unintentional mystification. One must assume that some authors quoted phrases from his works as illustrations of their thought, and so he was finally credited with the whole apparatus of alchemy.

Alchemy was continuing in the Islamic world on a steady and unexciting path, and was alive within the Byzantine ambit, but its real development was now as a philosophical and chemical discipline in western Europe. The mental attitude of the Europeans was in many ways like that of ancient Greece. There was a strong tendency to theoretical construction which only occasionally turned to practical experiment with a definite purpose. There was a great capacity for wondering about the universe and its meaning, and this crystallized into a kind of Christianized mythology. The chemical experiments derived from the Arabs became more important to most people than the contemplation of processes already well known. Instead of experimental alchemy being a type of mystic contemplation, it took form as a search for practical systems of purifying metals until they revealed their true nature by sloughing off all accretions and showing themselves to be the purest of perfect gold. Every newly discovered substance or combination of substances attracted attention and immediately became the subject of experiment to determine its possibilities. Useful and important scientific discoveries in chemistry arose from this discipline, including the discovery of gunpowder. Through their practical advances in the science of matter, the alchemists outstripped the classical world from which their art derived its mystical origins.

Yet there was always a mystical side to this alchemy. The material side had not taken over completely in the fourteenth century and it was still apparent to the serious researchers that the alchemist was himself part of the work. This was not a defensive action to separate the adept from the charlatan, but an inherent part of the method. The personality of the experimenter must be consonant with the nature of the work. The work was the purification of the world of matter so that its golden nature should be revealed. The material must be subjected to all kinds of symbolic tribulation before the last change came. The latter was not effected from the matter itself, but through the addition of the agent of transmutation, the Philosopher's Stone. Some experimenters said they found this to be a red powder; but generally in literature we find it to be an ineffable substance, in itself solid, liquid, earth and metal.

It is rare for any two accounts of the final agent of transmutation to agree. However, in the fourteenth century it was more common to expect this wonderful substance to take a solid form. Perhaps this was due to the increasing understanding of the physical side of nature. The essences, the vaporous exhalations, even the fine dust of calcination must be brought to a solid state. It was quite reasonable that the wonderful stone should be a solid. But it must also be fluid in its nature for it must permeate all the body of material it was to change. Hence reason dictated a very fine powder, the flour, or flowers of the Stone (a term used in the way that we still use 'Flowers of Sulphur', for finely powdered sulphur). In the case of the greatest of fourteenth-century alchemists, Nicolas Flamel, the transmutant was prepared in the alembic from a careful burning and distillation, and close observation of colour changes. The white and the red elixirs were prepared and gave the desired results in the crucible. Yet Flamel's account is almost like the description of a vision, and the gold produced at the final trial of the red stone was a soft and exceedingly malleable gold. Maybe this was a kind of amalgam. We do not know. However, the later legend that Flamel blew up his home through the use of a red powder is a transmutation of the facts. After his death there was a rumour that some of the wonderful powder was to be found in his home, so there was a raid on the building. It was stripped down to the cellars, and certainly must have looked as if it had been blown up. One story tells of a crucible with a button of gold in it, but that is equally likely to be an appropriate invention.

The story of Flamel, however, has much more important elements than the existence or not of a specimen of gold. He shows the character of the alchemist better than almost any other practitioner of the art.

Nicolas Flamel was a scholar and a particularly skilled scrivener. He prepared books, wrote documents for customers, and employed a staff of skilled copyists who, in those days before printing, enabled him to make a very good living as a bookseller. Since few people had the skill to read and write he was a man of social importance and had many business contacts with the nobility around the court in Paris. Maybe he was particularly interested in gold from the point of view of an illuminator of manuscripts. His description of the perfect malleability of alchemical gold almost suggests this. In any case we must remember that Flamel was a good business man and one who could inspire great works of art of the kind we see in late fourteenth-century Books of Hours. He was rich and respected.

Flamel had no great opinion of his own importance. Even though he sought out knowledge of alchemy it was not for the increase of his wealth. If there was alchemical gold behind his benefactions to the Church there need not have been any great amount involved, since, as E. J. Holmyard pointed out, the probability was that the Flamel fortunes were sufficiently large for his benefactions to have been made in the way of straightforward business. He showed a certain austerity in personal matters, and, as an alchemist, was always careful to live simply and dress in plain clothes without ostentation. He was always very careful to pay his workmen well, and left benefactions to some of them. In fact the workshops of Nicolas Flamel, scribe and publisher, were a small image of the best principles of the commercial world which was to succeed the feudal state some five centuries later. The very lucrative enterprise depended on the whole staff benefiting from its progress. The human relationships were good, and based on the principles of Christian teaching. Similarly, the marriage of Nicolas Flamel to Pernelle was something very special. They met in middle age, for Pernelle was over forty at the time. She was a careful and skilled manager of the housekeeping for the whole enterprise. Their love story is not explicit, but one senses a unity of heart which is rare and precious. After her death Nicolas Flamel waited another twenty years before he too was buried in the church of St Jacques near their home. If such a character was a *sine qua non* for the successful alchemist there is little wonder that there are few in history.

Flamel's introduction to alchemy was through an archetypal dream, which also had the quality of time-stepping. The vision of an angel holding a strange book with unrecognized characters was obviously an intimation of impending crisis and change. The promise that he should later understand the book seemed strange, since he had no idea what it was and the vision merely departed in a blaze of light, which itself was a rare experience of psychological advance. Yet a few days later Flamel saw the very book offered for sale in Paris. It was bound in copper sheets and the pages were of very thin bark (this was probably papyrus) with a drawing on every seventh page. The lettering was drawn with a stylus and it was written in Latin. Thus in 1357 Nicolas Flamel came into possession of *The Book of Abraham the Jew* of which he had recently experienced a pre-vision.

Here one halts a moment to wonder if there was any real connection between this work and the many works which later went under its name. Flamel described the pictures in it, and so they appear again and again, but he did not divulge the text. What is offered is always so confused that one finds it hard to accept that the copies are anything more than imaginative reconstructions by later alchemists whose hopes were greater than their understanding. Flamel's other remarks make one think that he was dealing with one of the works of the Jewish community in Alexandria in the first century AD. Was it the original, a copy, or even a time-jumping apport? There is just that fascinating intrusion of the irrational in the story which leads one to sense something abnormal about the circumstances. Even the paintings, though in the full alchemical tradition, do not fit in with the description of the text. Were they later additions?

# Medieval France

A French illustrated Biblical commentary of the fourteenth century. The pictorial material includes many subjects which recur frequently in alchemical works with parallel meanings. This page shows the strong castle protecting the Jewel, and Balaam on his ass

Oblacio ihu in templu huis par turtur
in manib. Luce .2. s. capm
Apredca cap audim quo xps fuit mag horatus
I seqnti audiem quo i templo fuit dno psntat
Quadragesima die post xpi natuuitate
Pegit bm uirgo puisicadis sue sollempnitate
Et ipa no fuit necesse depuisicacione
Que recepit filiu sine uirili mixtiõe
Voluit ni puisicadi: pageir uitu legis exeqt
Et exprimatrix legis ee iudicetur
A maria quor iuutes cardinales i se hebat
Preuaricatrix legis nequaqã erat
Na oia que legis erant diligentissime tenebat

Archa sps calibi uga z urna. Exodi .16.
Qua ppr ipa ē archa testamti sps figurata
In qua includit erat oia legis mandata
I narcha eni erat due tabule lapidee moysi
Inquib: scpta erat decem precepta dei
Que xps iterauit z audientiu uultuãit H annotabo
Sub breui quada glosula H describabo
Primu ē deos alienos no adorabis
Id ē deu ueru coles z supi eu nichil amabis
S cdm no assumes i uanu nom dei tui
Id ē no blasphemes ni iurab idebite noie suo
Tciu ē memeto ut diem sabbati scisices
Pls leo mlituros nõ ptes z opa aliena uices
Ciu honora pntes tuos ipis debite obiendo

Ecclesia mistudo z aialõ eor miserando
Cintu ē no occides exp illo neglgit cogitatu
Aurilio ysilio malo exeplo n aliq occasio
Sextu ē no metabis indek opando cogitat
Nec medite tua fornicadez aliis sustinedt
Septu n lumbis aliena ē mo q lib: appetido uet
Octauu derelias i iuuo suo dno erudicta ueni
O ctauu ē falsu testioniu n psumciui ni
Ad dei onie medacisz dolu z detcdem deuit
Nonu ē couui l agri pxi tui no debe desidrar
T aliud delic meter quelles z ai dãpno suo ad
Decimu ē uxore pxi i acilla pxi no scupiscea
Precedens dere i mobili id de mobili i telligat
Vnr duo ultima precepta i illo iudicat dist
Et sic qz res mobiles z immobiles uoluit d
Oia ista mãdata maria diliger absuuab
T ideo i archa testamti ipa figuratur Bibliu
Archa testamti etiã libu legis cotinebat
T maria libros sacre scpture librus hebat
I narcha erã uga aaron que quodã slouui
Et maria slouuit iuxtã oes simul pul
Archa etiã urnã aurea cumãna tenebat
T maria ueru mãna celi nob offebat
Archa testamti de ligno techo spuebli ua fu
T maria ipuidine ut i pulucre nesqd erõ
Archa quor oatos áuros statib habeba

Joseph rejected by his brethren is cast into the well. Jonah is thrown to
Behemoth to appease the storm

The angels bring succour. The king and the eagles

*Opposite:* The presentation of the baby Jesus in the Temple. The angels cense
the tree of life which is the Gospels

The Resurrection. Daniel in the fiery furnace

The Harrowing of Hell. The lion adversary driven away

Nicolas Flamel (1330–1417), Parisian
alchemist, was buried in the church of
Saint-Jacques-la-Boucherie (*below*),
near which he lived and worked. At the
end of the eighteenth century the church
was demolished, but the tower (*right*) is
still standing; it is now a meteorological
station. Flamel's tombstone can be seen
in the Musée de Cluny in Paris

The title-page of *Alchimie de Flamel* emphasizes the religious nature of the work

Opposite above: Three stages in the Process, linked with the equivalent symbols

Opposite below: The furnace and alembic; the mercurial serpent crucified

The furnace and the symbols of minerals to be used

Le Jeune ☿ est L'Eau du Rosier qui fleurit a mesure qu'il s'anime

Le Jeune ☿ soit dominиу par son poids de 10♃ de plus que les 2 autres ensemble

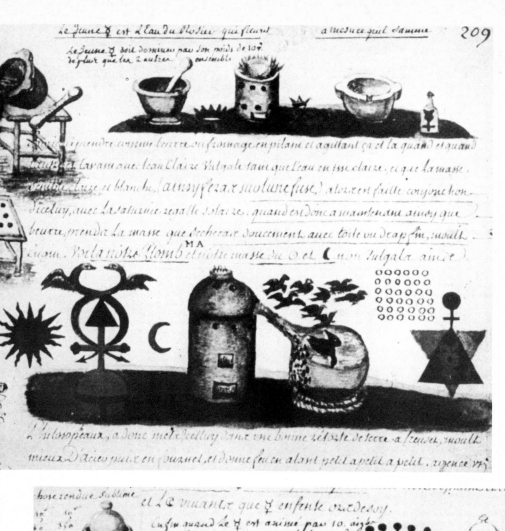

... prendre comme beurre ou fromage en pilant et agittant ça et la quand et quand ... et lavant avec l'eau claire vulgate tant que l'eau en soit claire, et que la masse semble claire et blanche, (ainsi fera sa nature fixe) alors en faille conjonction d'icelluy avec la saturnie regalle solaire. quand est donc a maintenant ainsy que beurre, prends la masse que dessecheras doucement avec toile ou drap fin, moult ... Voila nôtre Plomb et nôtre masse de ☉ et ☽ non vulgate ...

L'interposeaux, a donc mele d'icelluy dans une bonne retorte de terre a feuer, moult mieux D'accus puis en gourmel, et donne feu en alant petit a petit a petit. Digence ...

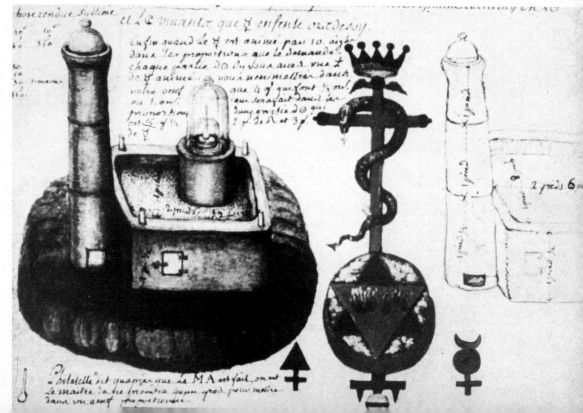

el LC muante que ☿ enfente eue de soy.

... Phitelette dit que quiqer que le MA est fait, on est le maitre de la re prendre qu'on proit pour metre dans un œuf proportion ...

2 pieds 6 ...

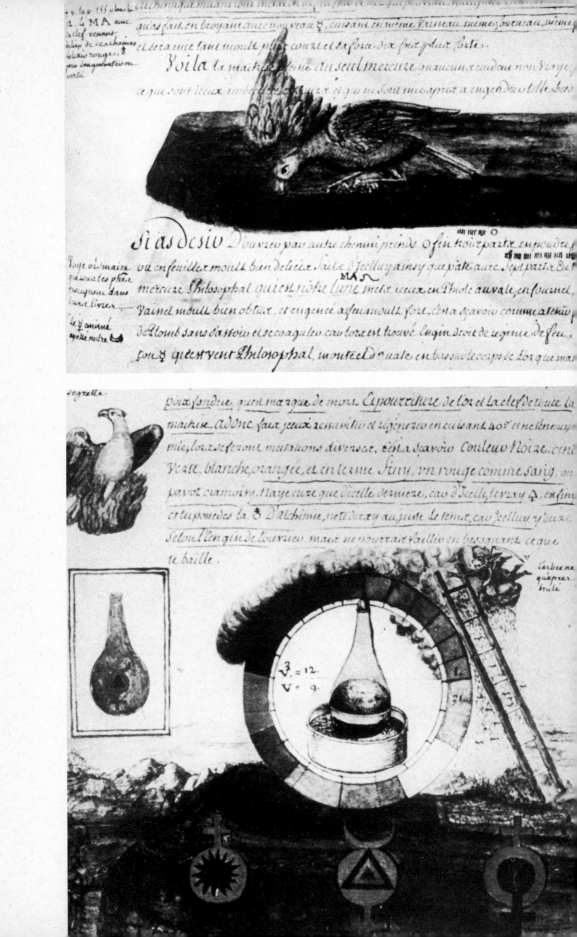

# Multiplication

Advise donc que si as desir de Multiplier la poudre. Prends d'icelle une part et l'arose de deux parts de ton mercure animé, cuite comme as fait en phiole après ainsi fait d'iceux pâte molle et douce, même fourneau, même feu et ore en plus petit de temps se sera fait le deuxieme tour de la zone philosophale, alors la poudre est vigoree de 10. fois plus fort que N'étoit la prime naissance d'icelle.

Fais encore icelle tourner voire même tant que tu voudras et sera alors achevé le trésor ja sans prix qui est sur tout le monde entier le meilleur que ne puis ja desirer icy bas, car as santé et richesse si en vre comme en metieu; adonc as le trésor de toute ta félicité mondaine que moy pauvre rural de Pontoise a y faitte et maistricé par hoir reprise en ma maison rue des Ecrivains tout proche la chapelle St Jacques de la boucherie, et que moy Nicolas Flamel te baille pour l'amour qu'ay envers tous en l'honneur de Dieu pour Sa gloire et louange du Pere, fils et Saint Esprit et sacré trinité que je prie de maintenant t'illuminer et te vouloir conduire dans le chemin de vérité et de lumière ainsi que dans la voye du salut. Amen soit-il.

The symbols of the process of multiplying the powder of transmutation

The wounded bird (calcination)
The distillation of minerals from below the earth to the vapours of the sky

Philosophy has dominion over the rocks (inert matter)

Melusina in the central waters, surrounded by the four elements, lifts the chalice with the dragon

The extension of
the mercurial
caduceus to the
influence of
Venus and Mars

The planets
around the pillar
of life. Note the
prescribed
planetary
situation for
each stage of the
development

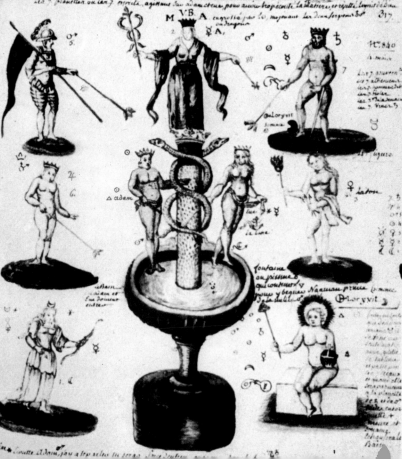

Mercurius halts the stroke of time

The winged caduceus of Mercury,
the jewel of double wisdom

*Opposite:* The instruments: furnace,
alembics, scales, bellows etc

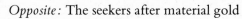

The living tree flourishes amid
astrological danger

The mercurial serpent is crucified

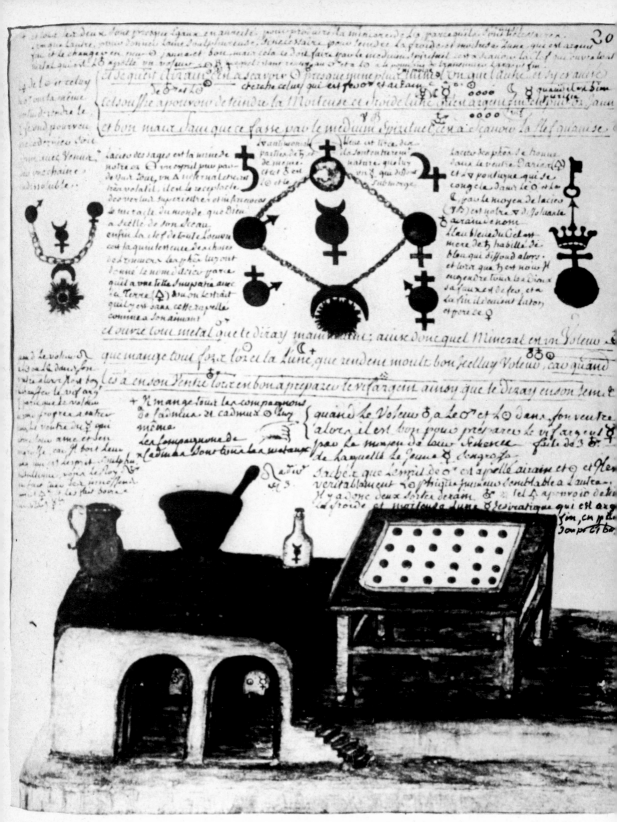

The arrangement of laboratory furniture for the furnace and a planetary-metallic diagram

Flamel was so puzzled by what had happened that he became unwell. His wife came to know of the problem and, practical as usual, persuaded him to seek advice. They made copies of the drawings in the book and exhibited them. This brought an alchemist into their life, but his translation and explanation was quite impracticable. It was only after nine years that Flamel was able to visit Spain where eventually he met a converted Jew who was also a student of the *Kabbalah*. They set out together to see the book in Paris, but the adept was taken ill and died, after giving Flamel sufficient clues to interpret the obscurities of the Latin text. In Paris Flamel and Pernelle worked with the usual furnaces and vessels and followed the routines prescribed. It took seven years to complete the work. Then they found a brilliant white elixir, which transmuted lead to silver. After this the process continued, through the expected sequence of colour changes, until the Flamels had the red elixir which was used to transmute some mercury into a wonderfully soft and ductile gold. It is clear that Flamel and Pernelle made few transmutations. When Pernelle died in 1397, forty years after the discovery of *The Book of Abraham the Jew*, they had made three transmutations in five years. That was all, and it was understood that all the money value of the gold was used for religious charities in Paris.

We have here a picture of a world in which the alchemical experiment was possibly, but by no means certainly a success. It took much time, and was performed by two people deeply attached to each other, and deeply involved in religious exercises and charitable works in addition to their creative business interests. France was involved in war over the whole period of their lives, first suffering from the English invasion and later reorganized by the resurgence of French power. The final political dénouement was to come after Pernelle's death. There was undoubtedly a period of uncertainty and strain in Paris at the critical period of the alchemical story.

The vision of the book is remarkable and opens many questions to which no answers can be given without information which we do not possess. The two people concerned were already well integrated and spiritually developed before they followed the instructions conveyed in the book's mysterious phraseology. How much they suffered, and what they felt they had gained by the experience is not known to us. To their contemporaries they seemed to be good and holy people who had made and spent a great deal of money, and who most probably had the secret of the Philosopher's Stone. Hence the destruction of their home beside the Church of St-Jacques-la-Boucherie. The only surviving relic is the tombstone of Nicolas Flamel which is characteristic of his writings. The Tour-St-Jacques is all that remains of the church, and its beauty shows well enough why Flamel and Pernelle loved the church so well. Meanwhile the tower has become a meteorological observatory, which seems to be pleasantly appropriate.

While the Flamel episode was taking place in Paris there was considerable interest in alchemy all over Europe. In England there was so much evidence of confidence-trickery that the performance of alchemical experiments was limited by a system of Royal Licences, of which a few were granted in the hope of obtaining treasure to prosecute the French wars. There is no evidence of success. In fact we gain a very good picture of the intelligent Englishman's attitude to alchemy in the works of a Civil Servant turned poet, Geoffrey Chaucer. A little analysis of the material in *The Canon's Yeoman's Tale* is of interest.

Chaucer's alchemist was a Canon in the Church. That is to say that he was a learned man who was well acquainted with books and whose knowledge was suited to a fairly high office. He had a faithful yeoman serving him, though at the last this servant was deeply distressed at their continual and miserable failures. He decided to tell the Canterbury Pilgrims of the desperate shifts to which the Canon resorted in order to get more gold by cheating and confidence tricks. Noting the risk of exposure, the Canon took flight and left the yeoman to continue the tale. It is quite clear that these English alchemists had set out with a book of rules to find the Philosopher's Stone or elixir by honest means in order to perform transmutations. They failed, partly because it was impossible, in those times, to get apparatus which would stand the temperatures and pressures involved:

> Ful oft it falleth so,
> The pot tobreketh and farewel all is go.
> These metales ben of so gret violence,
> Our walles may not make hem resistance,
> But if they weren wrought of lime and ston;
> They percen so that thurgh the wall they gon;
> And som of hem sinke doun into the ground,
> (Thus have we lost by times many a pound)
> And som are scattered all the flore aboute;
> Som lepen into the roof withouten doute.

Each failure only drew the people concerned into a discussion of the reasons, and then they tried once more. They ran into debt, borrowing so much that they feared they could not repay their creditors in a lifetime. Even the Canon, who must have enjoyed a reasonable stipend, was in rags when he met the Pilgrims. The yeoman was yellow skinned and unhealthy through his continual exposure to the heat from the furnaces, and the fumes of the materials they used which included mercury and its poisonous compounds.

This is indeed a shocking contrast to the history of Nicolas Flamel. In the whole Chaucerian story there is no mention of philosophy or meditation as part of the practice of alchemy. It had become a kind of science which was seeking a specific substance to alter base metal into the noble metals. The parting of the ways had been reached. The knowledge of the philosophers had been made available to the greedy. Much misery and evil came of it. This state of affairs was to continue for the succeeding three centuries. The search for the Philosopher's Stone, which was also thought of as the elixir and the universal solvent, became a passion which acted upon a number of individuals like an addictive drug. It was rather more than a gambling fever, but akin to it, and the stakes were so high that too often they included other people's property.

It is clear from the end of the story that Chaucer was well acquainted with the literature of alchemy since he quotes from material in the well known *Secreta Secretorum* which purported to contain Aristotle's instructions to Alexander on the art of transmutation, set out in true alchemical style and attributed to Hermes as the originator of the art. He concludes with the thought that since this manuscript says that God alone has the secret knowledge, and that He will impart it only to the few whom He has chosen to have the knowledge, there is no reason to think that the ordinary alchemists had such knowledge.

Chaucer does, however, give us a very good list of the materials used by alchemists in his day: sundry vessels made of earth and glass, urinals, descensories, vials, crosslets, sublimatories, cucurbites and alembics; rubifying water, bull's gall, arsenic, sal ammoniac, and brimstone, and herbs including agrimony, valerian and moonwort.

There was a special water for albification (whitening), used after the materials had been subjected to calcination in the furnace. It apparently contained unslaked lime, chalk, and white of egg.

He also mentions various powders, dung, piss and clay. (These were used by alchemists in a special bath in which they fermented to make a steady slow heat; no doubt they seemed less offensive to people used to the foul state of town streets at the period.) There were also dried packets of material including saltpetre and vitriol. Wood and charcoal were used for the furnace fires. Sal tartare, alkali and salt were prepared and used for combustion and coagulation. Clay vessels strengthened with hair and oil were used with tartar, alum, yeast, brewers' wort, and fine potters' clay together with realgar (red arsenic), which were slowly incorporated in the vessels. All this was part of the citrination of silver, and used in the cementation and fermentation of ingots, and for making tests. There were four spirits: Mercury, Orpiment, Sal ammoniac, and Sulphur; seven metals: Sol (gold), Luna (silver), Mars (iron), Mercury (quicksilver), Saturn (lead), Jupiter (tin), and Venus (copper). So much was used to so little purpose. One notes that chemically the Alexandrians were surpassed by the Arabs, and that the latter were really the masters of the knowledge which had filtered through to Chaucer.

Thus we find at the end of the fourteenth century a complete acceptance in Europe of the process which had been transmitted via the Arabs. It had crystallized in a rather more material form, and so through its very weakness and failure it was to become the parent of experimental chemistry. On the other hand the philosophy attributed to the Greeks and Hermes was sifted through Arab and Byzantine sources. The medieval Christians had their own approach to thought and imbued it all with a richer sense of the relationship between the will of God and the mind of the adept. But there were few adepts who were willing to seek wisdom in waiting. Prayer and meditation and the search for simplicity were right for Nicolas Flamel, but not at all well regarded by the frustrated experimenters. It appears that the adept in the Hermetic mystery had to be a person who had been through the crucible of life just as had the materials he used for transmutation. In the years to come, it remained the property of the few to live the life of dedication and adoration which it demanded.

# 6

# CRYSTALLIZATION

The opening of the fifteenth century was an important period for European history. National states were taking form and achieving a balance of power which was crucial for the development of a new kind of social structure. Alchemy was becoming more and more European in its scope. The Asian countries were cut off by the development of the Turkish Empire. While Islamic alchemy continued as a viable tradition within the Turkish realms it ceased to advance, and was influencing Europe less and less. Meanwhile the decline of Byzantium was releasing more and more material through the migration of scholars to the West, and in particular the Italian states became centres of growth for new ideas which assumed an increasingly classical aspect. The actual improvement in educational facilities, the multiplication of books, and the emergence of learned men working in parallel with the ecclesiastical powers were features of culture which allowed a wider dissemination of alchemical ideas.

As the century developed there occurred a total alteration of emphasis in European culture. The West became officially crystallized into powerful states, but the divisions were minor rifts in a total cultural growth which was uniform. This uniformity was usually clearly recognizable at the end of the century when, as Byzantium fell to the Turks, Cordoba fell to the Spaniards. From Vienna to Gibraltar there was a Christendom, united and active. New emphases arose socially because of the development of internal trade and the later development of transoceanic voyages. Gold was more important because the active new states needed reserves of wealth to finance works of prestige as well as of war. Traders and bankers made the world of commerce something new. The new social groupings brought new opportunities for learning in the secular world.

Through all the turmoil of development the alchemists continued with their traditional routines. In some ways they were becoming fossilized. It was the puffers, the seekers after transmutation for wealth's sake, who became prominent. The philosophers were regarded with some awe, but their position as wise solitary experimenters was not threatened. A few left works on the alchemical art which are of importance. However, they were not interested in saying the same things as each other about the primary material, neither were any of them willing to betray the great secret by writing it down with simplicity as a kind of scientific text book. The fact is that they were not able to see the doctrine of their mystery in material terms. 'The gold of the Philosophers is not common gold,' was their saying. Puffers and other foolish people thought that this was just a way of saying that alchemical gold was more pure materially than everyday coinage. Even nobles and princes managed to seize the occasional philosopher and imprison him in the hope that he would fill their iron-bound chests in the state treasury. But it was not often that anything resulted beyond injury and disgrace.

The actual procedure of the alchemist had altered a great deal since the days of Maria Prophetissa with her *kerotakis*. The gold was not to be deposited in one vessel any more. Apparatus for distillation and fermentation had multiplied (an interesting by-product was the discovery of alcohol). The idea was not to produce gold *ab initio*, but to prepare the wonderful powders which would become the Philosopher's Stone and transmute lead to silver and mercury to gold. First one had to begin with the Primal material. This was not any atomic simplicity, but really the confused mass from which earth and its wondrous treasures were created. Probably three millennia earlier the Egyptian priests understood this as the black silt teeming with the spores of living things brought down by Hāpi, the Nile God, at the annual flooding of Egypt. But by medieval times the ideas were direct; one must search for the commonest or most despised of substances. There was much dispute and uncertainty. Human ordure, decaying matter of all kinds, various herbs which had a reputation for magic, some kinds of rock, milk, semen; all kinds of things thought to represent the beginnings of nature were used. Sometimes they were mixed into a horrid witches' brew and cooked in a thick and strong flask. This was done only at the right conjunctions of planets in appropriate zodiacal signs. The universe was all part of this mystery and one had to seek to bring every aspect of the creation into line, for nothing less than the purification of nature herself was intended. In the vessel, warmed in its bed of fermenting manure, one might see the changes of fermentation and putrefaction going on. At the right stage when the raw unpurified matter was ready for the change it was moved to the furnace, and slowly the heat was built up. Then the mass separated into its four elemental states. Earth remained below ever darkening and condensing, becoming heavier and heavier. Air was driven off as vapours, black, grey, white and perhaps coloured, depending on what was in the vessel. Water bubbled and was later re-deposited by a distillation which must have seemed like magic; and then suddenly one would see the appearance of Fire from the elemental mass, as unknown gases ignited. This was a wonder of great importance.

The alchemist never neglected at every step in the process to read the best of the traditional works which he could find to guide him in the quest. He was a Christian and, in this great work of discovering the beauty of the wonders of nature, he remembered *The Song of Solomon* and the liturgy of the Church. The work was accomplished with prayer and religious devotion. For the true adept the unity of the creation was being demonstrated in a particular way. The elements which had now separated were also opposites. Fire and water do not mix, and how can one reconcile air with earth? The seven days of Creation were remembered with wonder. Here was a sign of the power of the Most High.

Under such circumstances, developing in a steady process over weeks and months, the alchemist was not seeking a scientific approach at all. The chemical knowledge was a by-product. To some it was important, but never was it an essential to the process. All the mythological archetypes appeared. The alchemist was expressing thoughts from deep within himself, of which he saw only the outward manifestations. The green dragons and the white and red lions were, at the same time, material substances and visionary figures. He was in no state of mind to hold strictly to the narrow path of rationality. All his work was in quest of a mystery; he opened his very soul to the impact of half formulated ideas and saw the facts interpreted as visions. However he was quite aware of the material side. It was important for him to use the right substances, to apply heat for the right times, to have vessels of the right capacities and bellows of the right size. His interpretation of all the events was conditioned by tradition and not by deductive logic. He was obliged, if he were to be a true alchemist, to follow the preparation and meditations of earlier adepts. He was sure that in the boiling fiery mass he was witnessing elemental struggles personified as lions and dragons. He had to realize that in his own life the process of purification might be as painful and as rewarding as the struggle within the sealed vessel above the furnace. Eventually came the *nigredo*, the blackening. The matter lay a black inert mass under the dews and vapours above. Often here there was a halt for a repetition, in which the distillates were returned to the black mass. The spirit of life returning to the decayed corpse was the picture in the mind, and the prayers said reflected the theme of the desire for purification of the corrupt and broken body.

71

Then came a re-distilling, sometimes repeated hundreds of times, always with the danger of a wrong heating of the furnace and an explosion which would destroy the whole work. Patience and more patience, and Job-like acceptance of sufferings, was the only way. It was a hard way because new materials had to be obtained and most difficulty was experienced in acquiring the necessary strong glass and ceramic vessels. One could not lead people to think that there was gold to be acquired by a raid on the laboratory. However, money had to be found and excuses given. At this point many a serious student of philosophy became a puffer for the sake of gain which might help him to continue his private work of the redemption of matter.

If the work had progressed well, both with the stars and the meditations, a time for the final experiment would be reached. The dews distilled and the flames reflected fell on the black mass, which reddened and glowed, and then whitened. So it always was, and there was no surprise in the first change of colours. Yet they had their mystical significance for the adept. The regulation of the bellows was now particularly significant for the final change was to be timed by the heavens. Man alone could not prepare what was to happen. Everything moved towards the appearance of a most beautiful whiteness. Then came the Phoenix, the strange flashing white jewel, the flower, the expanding feathers of white fire. The process halted. Something was taken from the vessel, and if it was poured on an ingot of lead melted in the nearby crucible there would be a sudden whitening and brilliance which would leave behind it an ingot of silver. The white elixir had been achieved.

Then for those who dared the process was continued. The white became red, then golden, then it burst into a coruscation of colour, the Peacock's Tail. This was the prelude to something indescribable, a blueness, a whiteness, a darkness which was brighter than light. At the moment of this happening the process halted. What remained was the red powder, the true Stone which was not a stone, the Philosophic Water which was blue and not water, the mystery which, dropped into a crucible of quicksilver, would transmute it entirely to gold.

All alchemists expected this; they desired the experience more than the continuance of life. Few achieved it. It was repeated in books, was claimed by charlatans, and resounded in the minds of men through centuries. Yet there are few accounts which can be said to have any sound basis in fact. None of them have any chemical facts to support them. Modern scientists point out clearly enough that these things just would not work in any laboratory that we know. True they have never tried the utterly irrational task of distilling and redistilling matter some five or seven hundred times. Yet something

*A section of the fourth* Ripley Scrowle, *showing the Melusina descending on the tree of life to bring wisdom to Man and Woman*

Lingua Sapientie

Lignum Vite

phÿloso-
phie pa-
radisus

ineffable occurred for the true alchemist. The opposites in nature had been reconciled. Earth, Air, Fire and Water were at one in a mysterious object, which had the divine power added to it so that it could transform base matter into its noble perfection as gold and silver, the representatives of sun and moon, the dual powers of male and female in the work of creation. Were these phenomena of static electricity? Did some strange combination of events bring the process to completion at some node in four dimensional space? Or was it all a blessed vision completing the long preparation? We simply do not know. The mind of the alchemist was always unusual and in the world of today it is impossible to understand its complexity.

As Professor Jung pointed out in his three large books on the subject, the alchemist reproduces in his work the whole experience of some people in our own times. This manifests itself in dreams and visions which mark the development of the personality as the ego takes its place in relation to the deeper forces of humanity stemming from the Unconscious. This process within the psyche (the totality of the being) leads to the establishment of the 'persona', which is a deeper and wider expression of the human being, including most of the unconscious forces which do not ever become clear to us. The process of individuation in this case is one of true union, the conjugation of opposites as in alchemy.

There can be no doubt that the typical visions of the alchemist were seen as occurring to the materials in the great work. With us they usually come as old age approaches, and are felt as visions within, transforming the character in just the way the alchemists hoped to transform the *materia prima* to the gold and silver of sun and moon. This expressed the alchemical idea of the universality of the Creation, which related man and matter with the sky and, ultimately, with the divine mind of the Creator.

Thus the philosopher, overwhelmed by his unknown discovery, had something which is common to mankind of all periods; but it was the jewel attained by few, and cannot be adequately explained. For those who had this jewel there was no easy life. The further path seems to have been of suffering and obscurity. As the alchemists so truly explained it was a jewel despised by mankind, and not to be given away or even shown to many because it would simply be rejected.

Social necessities, however, demanded that the strange experiments of the alchemist must be known to the people of the material world. Princes and prelates needed gold for their work of bringing civilization to mankind (too often a euphemism for having their own way). The poor 'puffer' had to be brought into the workshops of the court in case he found a way of making a scientific transmutation. Even Popes were involved in the search. Later the

73

Spaniards found a substitute by plundering Mexico and Peru, but in the fourteenth century there was anxiety to find the wonderful secret of making gold. Gold bought things, and so gave wealth to manufacturers and merchants. The development of European civilization demanded material wealth. So the puffer and the philosopher were brought in to seek the gold of this world; and the poor human soul was left to find its own way.

Very few alchemists seem to have discovered the secret for themselves. Many of them experienced visions and dreams in which the idea needed for success was revealed to them by a visitant in the form either of an old philosopher, or more often of an angel. Others seem to have advanced far along the path of chemical experiment and needed only the last step to be able to make the elixir. Then they would search for further knowledge of the secret process. It was not easy to interpret the deliberately confusing texts, and they were often disappointed. However, continuing steadfast in their quest, they were usually out travelling in search of knowledge, when they finally met a stranger who, after questioning them, took them to a laboratory and told them that they could have from his store some of the precious transmutant. In these tales the substance is usually a yellowish and waxy material, like a pebble, but with the hardness of horn so that with an effort a little might be scraped off. Two or three of the greatest alchemists experienced the discovery in this way. They never claimed to have made the discovery by their own intellectual effort. It sounds as if they had projected an archetypal vision which might have presented itself as an elderly philosopher; yet in most cases they were assured that the tiny grain of the elixir which was given to them transmuted many hundreds of times its own volume of lead into gold. Here we encounter again the idea of the fruitfulness in the union of opposites. The light and very small 'stone,' which is like wax and horn, transforms the heavy and earthy metal lead to pure shining gold. Some of them, at least, seemed to believe this was a real experience. In any case the matter is quite beyond investigation as far as we know, since the transmutation of metals is not apparently possible by chemical means, especially with no special laboratory apparatus except for furnace and crucible. Yet we find that the descriptions given to us by reputable scholars are presented with the most serious gravity. Perhaps it became the acceptable way of concealing other things, perhaps even the absence of the knowledge of the final secret.

Seen from the viewpoint of the mid-twentieth century, alchemy must be regarded as irrational. Yet there are the occasional hints that the phenomena were partially caused by electrical discharges, which were simply not understood in those days. Also we can have no doubt whatever that in the fourteenth century, and for two centuries following, the possibility of transmutation was accepted, and alchemical gold was frequently referred to in terms which implied its factual existence. One would say now that some matters remain which are not easily explained away. However, the view that most of the work of alchemists was really a projection of the difficult path along which man approached total unity of the personality is important. This psychological theory, so strongly advocated by C. G. Jung, has the very special merit of explaining the persistence of the alchemists in their studies, and of the quiet joyfulness which was the reward of the best of them. It also makes clear the necessity for medieval alchemy to divide into chemistry and philosophical alchemy. The attainment of an integrated personality is incompatible with the frantic desire for gold which drove many alchemists to confusion.

Among the more respected of the gold makers of the fourteenth century was John Dastyn, who wrote to Pope John XXII in defence of the alchemists who had been heavily penalized by a decretal of that Pope, reigning in Avignon. Dastyn's idea was that from the combination of natural substances one could make many extracts. From natural gold one should be able to extract a red sulphur which in itself was a sufficient elixir to transmute pure mercury into real gold. That a monk who was a scholar of some standing should open a dispute with the Papacy on the subject of alchemy in the first third of the fourteenth century is sufficient evidence of the advance of purely scientific thought at the time. It is not to be taken as a proof, because the argument is strongly based on tradition instead of experiment as were most works of the schoolmen. However, it was assumed by many people that the wealth of Pope John XXII at his death was of alchemical origin, perhaps because it was still not thought quite right that a Pope should be so deeply concerned with earthly riches. Dastyn was, however, well regarded and although he was in religious orders he was allowed to write on these subjects and to run his laboratory. One of his best ideas was that in a transmutation the elixir entered the spaces between the particles of matter, and that it was a fluid without any weight. It was as good as saying that it was of the nature of heat or electricity, since both these concepts were to be described as weightless fluids in later years.

But by the fifteenth century the whole subject of alchemy was expanding. Knowledge was open. The cheats and the plodding followers of tradition were to be found in any society. Probably the greatest of the traditionalists in the quality and quantity of his publications was George Ripley, who was not only a wealthy man of good family, but also an Augustinian Canon. He had studied widely, in Louvain, Rome and on the Island of Rhodes, making a great reputation as one learned in the science of his time, especially in the discipline of alchemy. The Knights of St John of Jerusalem gave him encouragement and a place to study. In return he made many benefactions to their order. In Bridlington, Yorkshire, where he was settled in the monastery from 1471, he continued his alchemical studies and was regarded as a nuisance, because the pungency of some of his compounds was remarkable, even in that unsanitary age. However, he is known more for his writing in English, and for his wonderful powers of pictorial imagination. The alchemical process becomes a vehicle for poetry in which the traditional figures of the King and Queen, the Green Lion, the Red Dragon, the Rose, and so on, are presented in a kind of play of sequences following the process through to the creation of the Phoenix. There were many editions of his work in manuscript, and it was not long before they became more available through the newly-developed technology of printing. From his collection of documents we have the exquisite *Ripley Scrowles* in the British Museum.

In Ripley the arts of the illustrator and the poet came to the service of the mystic. There is no solid evidence of his making gold, but we find a great deal of the nature of the dreams and traditional figures which filled the soul of a cultured alchemical thinker of his time. He does not lead us into the ordinary laboratory used by the puffers, though he used it and described all the processes. His vital contribution is in the interpretation of the routine events as a drama of the strange processes of nature, by which diversities and unities build up from simple materials, being combined and re-separated until a wonderful new kind of thing is created, which is the Phoenix, or the Stone, or the elixir. It has the God-given power of transmutation of baseness into a golden perfection. His work is precisely that of all the more important alchemists of the past, and shows little development, except that he is able to give a very good description of the process, seen through the thin veils of the images used to conceal substances from the vulgar gaze. He is quite unaware of the conflict between alchemical tradition and the orthodox views of the Christian community. If there is Manichaeism in his teaching, he sees it only as a pictorial image of the truth of religion. If the darkness and the light are one unity having two manifestations he is not aware that he has stepped a little beyond the Book of Job.

With Ripley we are at the end of the medieval period. The traditions are accepted and the visions seen; therefore the interpretation given by the previous masters was to be strictly observed. The future would be more questioning, and there would be no safe haven like the monastery at Bridlington. Ripley had used all the traditional material with brilliance. In his work the classical traditions of the Renaissance were clear. They were not a spur to further discovery, but a beautiful tradition which had to be followed because it was part of the early exposition of the subject. He had a typical ambivalence of belief in the revived thoughts of classical paganism. His attitude was romantic, and therefore the whole elegant conceit does not seem to be in contrast with the beautiful formality of Christian liturgies and Horae of his time.

In alchemical work Ripley was very much concerned in the observation of colour during the process. The appearance of a particular sequence meant the attainment of a stage in the process. It was as precise as the observation by a swordsmith of tempering colour in a blade. Each appearance indicated the appropriate poetic image of the process. It was a kind of meditation, although Ripley and his contemporaries appear to have thought of it as a fact being enacted before them. This makes understanding very difficult for us. Our prosaic attachment to observed demonstrable fact leads us to talk of metallic mercury instead of a grey wolf devouring the sun which is gold. So where the alchemist saw a drama we see a process of amalgamation. The Green Dragon is to us simply *aqua fortis*, a liquid which is so acid that it can even dissolve gold. Yet to the alchemist the picture conjured up in his furnace was much more important than an attempt to make a plain physical description. True, he was bound to secrecy and obscurity so that the great secret should not be betrayed to unsuitable people. Yet he really preferred the whole practical process to be part of the pictorial myth. One has no doubt that most of the images were archetypal and common to most of mankind. They occur in dreams with most of us in times of stress. The alchemist saw his visions as something outside his dreams, but we can share their content today. Only the young student seeing his first demonstration of mercury amalagamating with gold is likely to find the process reflected in a dream. To the alchemist the whole process was a living myth which was purifying the worker as it purified the sad, undifferentiated, and yet uncombined, *materia prima* with which he sought to work.

Once again it is necessary to remember that the alchemist was only very rarely a true scientist. His lineage was magical, going back to the beliefs of ancient Egypt as well as to the reasoning of the Greeks. So at the end of the fifteenth century and the dawning of a new world the path was to become more and more philosophical and less a strictly rational development of scientific metallurgy.

# 7

# ALBIFICATION

In the sixteenth century, which had begun with alchemy apparently firmly set in accepted frames of reference, the violence of political and social change eroded the formal patterns of life and made a new relationship between the alchemist and the public an accomplished fact. In a world in which one crisis followed another throughout history, the sixteenth century in Europe was notable for the quality as well as the force of its revolutions. The balance of political power was decidedly upset by the influx of material wealth from the Indies. The bounds of religious community life were violently disrupted. The dissemination of thought from the printed word became a commonplace. In Europe the division of the nations was deep. The violence of the Reformation and Counter-Reformation, and the tyranny of kings and generals was like the outward manifestation of a psychological breakdown. The shadowy side of the European culture burst out, overwhelming reason with emotional forces. Yet the débâcle of cultural values was accompanied by a general social advance. Cultural values recrystallized around individuals who were building a new society in their various ways. As for the alchemists, both puffers and philosophers had to rely on the support of princes rather than the security of the cloisters.

The general result of the changes was that alchemy suddenly came of age. The philosopher had to justify his work by results as well as by quoting tradition. He was really a more accomplished person because he was forced to delve into quite a number of other sciences to justify the propositions contained in his writings. The alchemical philosopher was safe from persecution if he was careful. He usually conformed to the local ruler's opinions, mostly because they didn't greatly concern him. His work was seen as an exploration of the forces of nature. Usually there was no suggestion that he was a necromancer or a witch. The general picture one obtains from the spate of books which appeared on the subject is of a learned man of some social standing, who sought the secret knowledge in a gentle humility. Yet the alchemist could also be the skilled trickster; for when one neglected the learned philosopher his other side, the man who had secrets to sell and tricks to play, was seen. The two combined in the Faust legend, but in fact the public view was that the learned philosopher was a scientist, although one to be treated with an awesome respect. The puffers were a source of amusement to those who ridiculed their ruinous enthusiasms, and a group of criminals to those who heard stories of their swindles.

True alchemists were forced to be circumspect in their behaviour in public, not only in the troubled earlier part of the century. The general attitude was towards concealment. The dangers were two-fold: uneducated people might take the scholar for a witch and bait if not actually assault him, or the local ruler might think the alchemist had the secret of making gold and imprison and even torture him in the hope of extracting information. We hear of very few alchemists who were able to lead a reasonably happy life. Yet such was the fascination of their subject that they continued to pursue it.

The fascination was largely psychological. The alchemist saw the process of creation reflected in his furnaces and alembics. At least that was his belief. To accompany his experience he read the works of previous alchemists, and meditated. Therein he found a new mythology which, although apparently Christian, included many opinions which would have been labelled Gnosticism or Manichaeism by the early fathers. This mythology has been shown by C. G. Jung to involve a great amount of outward projection of the contents of the unconscious mind. Actually the alchemist was experiencing induced waking dreams. The pattern of his experience was the pattern of the dreams and visions we may all experience during a normal life, when the usual sequence of crises in our development releases facets of our inner personality which are quite strange to us. The alchemist was reasonably sane and his mythology was based on ideas connected with his experiments. It has bequeathed to us some most wonderful illustrated manuscripts and books particularly from the sixteenth and seventeenth centuries when the world was developing into the new secular states. In the later part of the epoch we shall hear of the importance of sex in the whole philosophy. But at first, although sex symbolism was clear enough in the pictures, it remained suppressed. It appears that these learned men had found difficulty in facing up to the feminine *anima* image which was externalized as sulphur and moon, and mixed in the changeable hermaphroditic Mercurius.

One can easily understand that the impact of the mysteries which the alchemist projected in his work was so great that he could never abandon it without a complete breakdown. One does not face the totality of the self, or even begin to comprehend it without a great change in one's attitude to life. The narrow ego consciousness has to be accepted as a little part of oneself, though the only part which is clearly defined. The development of a greater unity of personality came to the alchemist because he was following a tradition and a myth which applied to all people. He had the secret knowledge without understanding that all this dramatic change was a matter within his own soul. He had no more control of it than we have of those disturbing dreams which trouble us from time to time in our own experience.

What had been happening through the centuries from the fall of Rome to the Reformation was the slow change of ancient cultist ideas from a mystery tradition into a new mythology. The only remains of the original cult were the attachment to the demonstration in the laboratory and the idea of purification of metals. The new mythology was something so deep in the minds of men that we can find its echoes in the northern myths as well as in the legends of the classical world. People dressed the inner visions in a pretty Renaissance costume and became divided over whether they were making gold or purifying the soul of the world. But there were not so many of them, in spite of the number of confused and confusing books which they diligently published.

The best scientific approach to alchemy was Thomas Norton's *Ordinall of Alchemy* of which many good copies exist. He was quite convinced that the Philosopher's Stone could be obtained, and that it would take some years to produce with the help of a team of four artisans. To help in his work Norton built himself a complex furnace through which, with the use of one fire box, he could heat a number of chambers to different intensities. He claimed to have discovered the Stone. According to local rumour, he produced gold to finance the rebuilding of St Mary Redcliffe, in Bristol, of which city he is said to have been Mayor. Yet he is perfectly clear in stating that the Stone is a gift of God to those who follow the true alchemical path. The power to discover this wonderful material came only to those who were prepared, and the result of the discovery was not inordinate desire for riches but a gentleness and sobriety, so that the understanding was enriched and the sense of personal importance chastened. The knowledge would enable one to face adversity with equanimity and to understand the ways of peace. True one could make gold through the knowledge but there were few who had the knowledge and they rarely made use of it, and then only for some very good purpose.

However, Norton's certainty that he could make the Stone by chemical methods was an argument for all those who followed. His warnings of the

# Artists and Patrons of Alchemy

A section from George Ripley's *Scrowles*. The dragon with its wings fixed to the chaotic material orb gives its blood for the making of the red and white stones and the elixir, the triple goal of alchemy

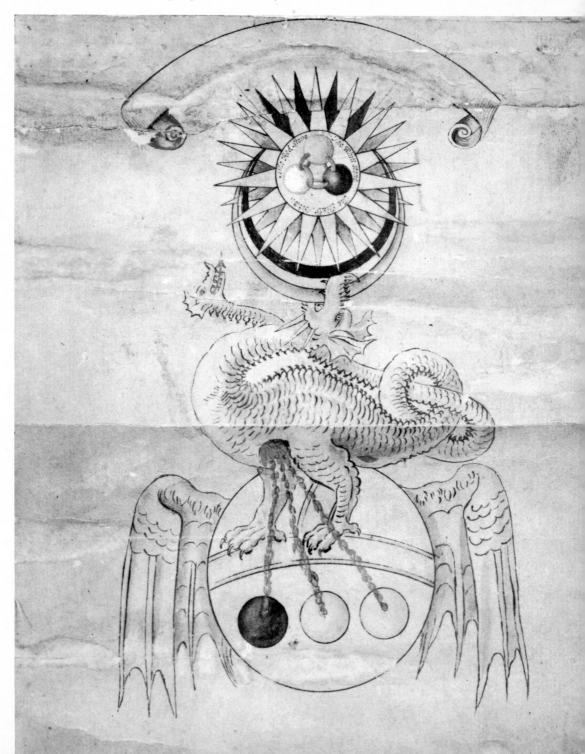

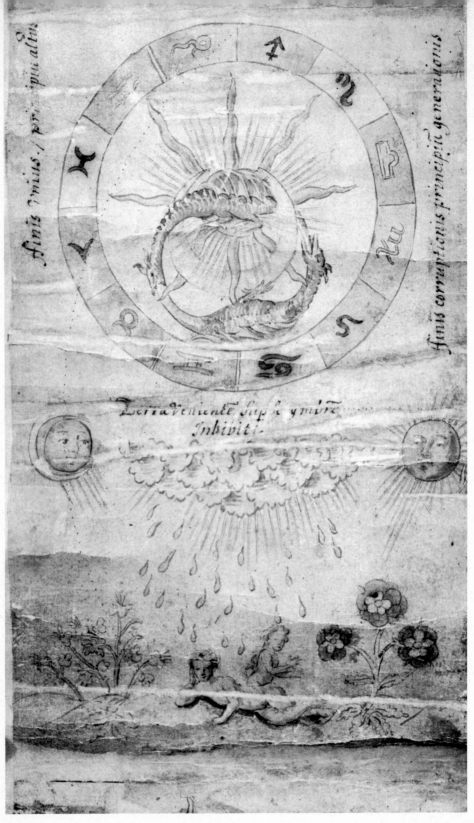

The completion of the alchemical work is here likened to the Creation. The dragons in the Zodiac complete time; fire and water cause flowers to bloom and Eve to emerge from Adam's side

The eternal unity of opposites: the tree of life where the sun is inspired by the
Spirit from above, the waters of life surrounded by the alchemists in which man
and woman find the fruitful vine

The title-page of George Ripley's *Cantilena*

The opening page of the *Cantilena* with parallel texts in Latin and English

*Cantilena Georgij Riplaj.*

1. En Philosophantium in hâc Cantilena
   Dans Arcana concina voce cum amæna,
   Quæ mentalis Iubilis pullulat avena,
   Vt Mens Audientium sit dulcore plena.

2. In Romanis partibus Nuptijs Mercurij
   Accidit post Studium semel quod interfuj,
   Vbj vescens epulis tam grandis Convivij
   Ignorata primitus hæc Novella didicj:

3. Quidam erat sterilis Rex in Geniturâ
   Cujus Forma Nobilis & decora pura
   Extitit; Sanguineus, pulchra qua natura;
   Attamen conqueritur sua contra Vira.

4. Rex et Caput Corporum quamobrem sum Ego,
   Sterilis, inutilis, sine prole dego:
   Gratis Influentijs Mundum ego Rego,
   Omniaq; nascentia Terra quod non nigo:

*George Ripley's Song.* X

Behold! and in this Cantilena see
The hidden Secrets of Philosophy:
What Ioy ariseth from y' Merry veins
Of Minds Elated by such dulcid Straines

Through Roman Countreys as Ione did p...
Where Mercuris Nuptiall Celebrated was,
And feeding stoutly (on the Bride-Groome...
I Learn'd these Novelties vnknown' befor...

There was a certaine Barren King by De...
Compos'd of the Purest, Noblest Earth,
By Nature Sanguine (which is fair) yet
Sadly Bewailed his Authoritie.

Wherefore am I a King, and Head of all
Those Men and things that be Corporiall?
I haue no Issue, yet (Ile not deny)
'Tis Mee both Heaven & Earth ar: Ruled by.

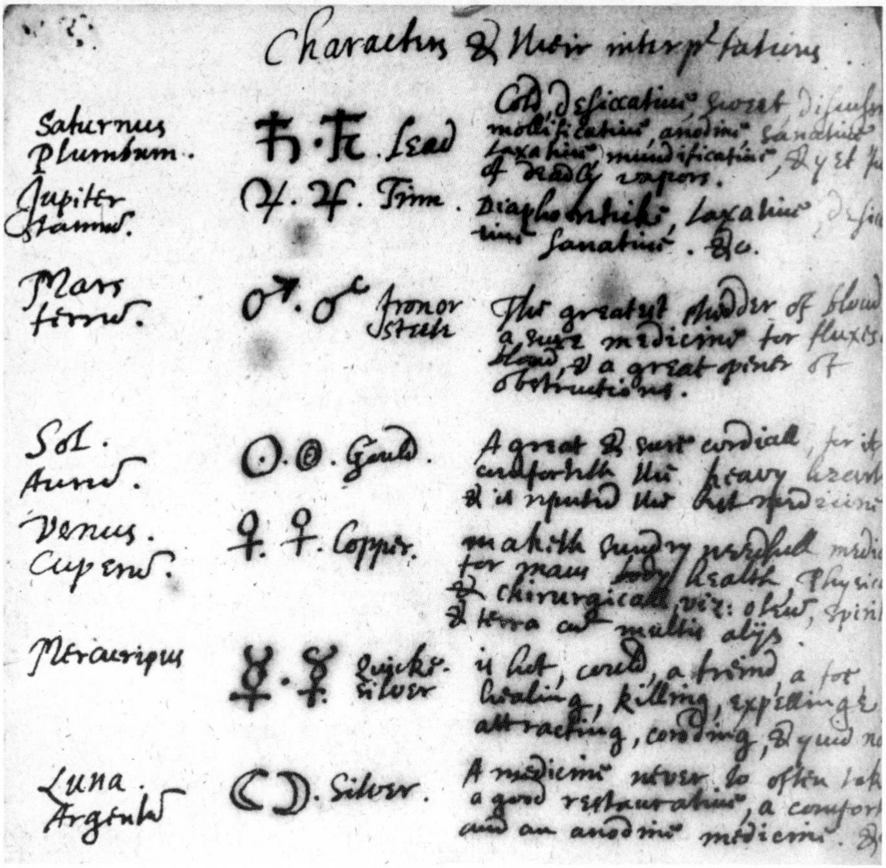

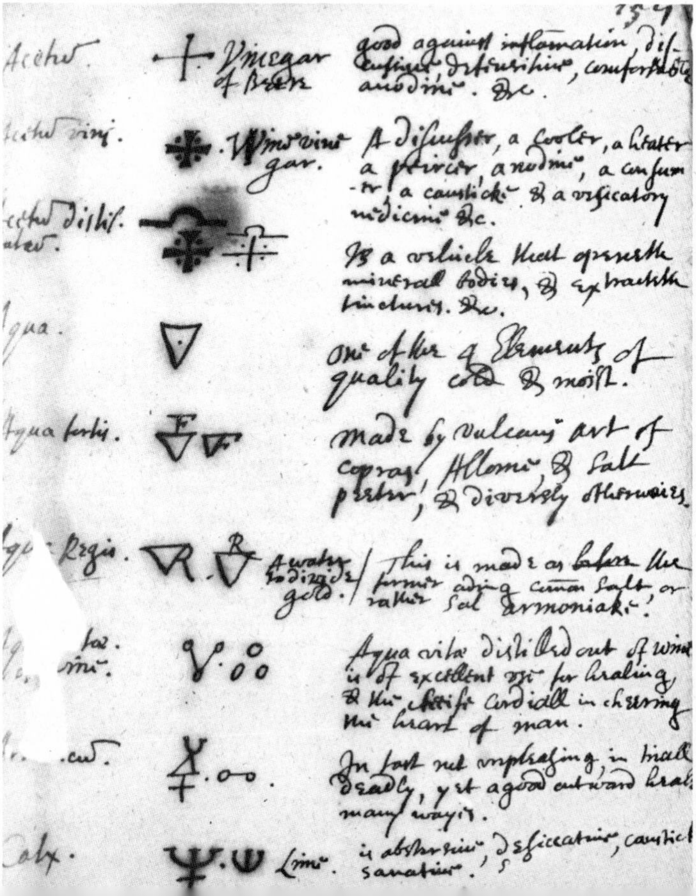

Symbols used by the
alchemists and their
interpretations, from a
seventeenth-century copy
of Ripley's *Cantilena*

Folios 25, 26, 27 from
*Splendor Solis*, a sixteenth-
century manuscript by
Salomon Trismosin containing a series of drawings
which shows Mercurius and
the Homunculus performing
the alchemical work

Portrait of Rudolf II, Holy Roman Emperor from 1576 until his death in 1612. He devoted much time to the study of alchemy, and often summoned alchemists to his court, where they would perform experiments for him. In the precincts of his castle in Prague is the 'Street of the Alchemists' (*below*) also known as 'Golden Lane'

futility of the search for those who wanted personal gain went unheeded;
only his laborious procedure and hard work for the transmutation were
followed. Many experimenters thought to ease the labour by using different
substances, on philosophical grounds, but they did not succeed. The reasoning of philosophy about chemistry was bound to fall down because it was
applied to substances from a mythological standpoint and not from truly
scientific measurement and classification. It even became possible for the
alchemist to have found the secret and then to lose the knowledge. Perhaps
one should attribute this to youth in the experimenter at the time of the first
discovery.

The classical case of forgetting comes in the story of the English alchemist,
Thomas Charnock. He learned his art from a master in Salisbury. The
master died in 1554, and Charnock continued a little while, but a laboratory
fire destroyed his apparatus. The alchemist was unable to continue with his
researches because there was no record and his memory failed him. It was
fortunate for him that the dispossessed Abbot of Bath was available to
re-educate him in the art. William Holway was now an old man, and blind,
but he knew enough of the secret to set Charnock on the right path again.
Unfortunately political circumstances and service in war frustrated Charnock
and caused him to break his apparatus when he was sent abroad. But this
time he had left a treatise on a long roll of parchment, which was not found
until a century later in the place where he had walled it up in his house. In
later life Charnock continued his studies and in the year 1579 he was
convinced that he had prepared the Stone. Before that date he had written
many alchemical works and had presented one of them to Queen Elizabeth 1
in 1566. However, Charnock had neither divulged any practicable process
of physical or chemical transmutation, nor had he used his knowledge to
enrich himself. He warned people from seeking gold for their own profit,
and even refused advice when it would have been profitable to have given it.
It appears that he too had achieved a peace of soul which transcended the
worth of material gold.

Paracelsus began to work and teach as a medical expert at the beginning
of the sixteenth century in Europe. He had a feeling for chemistry and its
possibilities which he developed into a chemical system of medicine. There
is no doubt that the man was a genius, brilliant, drunken, quarrelsome and
full of startlingly useful ideas. His view was that alchemy extended to all
chemical changes. His medical aim was to restore chemical balance in the
individual and in the internal organs. This, couched in a language of his own,
was a method of approach to the unifying of the individual. It put a
psychological truth in chemical terms. Thus Paracelsus, who invented his

own name, was a self-styled alchemist who did not seek to make the Stone, but to use his knowledge to make elixirs which would prolong life for his patients. One of the first of modern men, though in an outrageous guise, he stormed through a short life leaving books and ideas behind him which sealed the fate of the chemical side of alchemy. The mystic philosophy lingered on, but became more and more separated from the experimental process. Paracelsus, had however, brought about the possibility for the psychological processes involved in alchemy to be repeated in a more general context of the structure of the material world.

The alchemist was henceforward certain to move slowly out of the world of the natural sciences. The intellect was to take over many aspects of healing and knowledge of the material world. The empirical method of experiment for the purpose of finding out, rather than of repeating a ritual procedure, would gather strength for two centuries. It appears, from our present standpoint, to have been a necessary development. Mankind could not advance either materially or spiritually without understanding the processes of the natural world. The whole scientific method was reborn with a strength and fruitfulness which the thinkers of the classical world had not imagined. It is natural enough that it has led to a point of materialism and spiritual despair, for any process taken to extreme possiblities must reach a peak which is very lonely indeed. Today we are beginning to rediscover mysteries in the behaviour of matter, especially of the ultimate particles, which make one ponder on the possibility of matter proving to be non-material in its essence. We seem to be on the verge of an understanding which will give mankind the knowledge sought out by the alchemists, in a new form, with which they could not have coped. However, as we trace them in their period of rich philosophy and material decline we shall find much that is worthwhile.

The values in the new development of alchemy are much disguised by an element of magic. The usual story goes in a coach and four where the adept has a secret store of the red powder. This he has not prepared, but received from some older and greater master of the art. He uses his store before nobles and princes. When he casts it in a crucible of molten lead, or of purified quicksilver, the metal immediately becomes silver or gold – usually gold. He is usually a sober, studious type of person, though he travels in great state. His fate is either the fortunate one of retirement into obscurity in a little house of his own, or the more frequent one of being seized upon by some local potentate and imprisoned until he makes the last effort to escape and dies soon afterwards. The story persists with so many details of verisimilitude that it looks like one of those myths which have a habit of repeating themselves in real life. Its last victim seems to have been the unfortunate Comte de St Germain (see page 115).

Of the philosopher alchemists we have several examples of men who worked out theoretical structures which lead forward to a mystical art expressed finally in visions and symbols. Of the two their tradition is the more faithful though the less mysterious. They were at least producing lines of thought which bore fruit in a way of life and a search for the spiritual mysteries, though many of them were very curious individuals.

One of the earliest of the post-Reformation philosopher alchemists was Dr John Dee. For him the alchemical process was of comparatively little importance, for the whole realm of occult study was his field. He was a Prospero-like magician, though local children around his home at Barnes were of the opinion that he was a frightening old wizard. His passing acquaintance with the alchemical arts was largely through his contact with Edward Kelly, who is worth more study than is usually given to him. It is usually assumed that because he had his ears cropped for some early mis-demeanour he was a hardened fraud and trickster. How such a man could have imposed himself on the learned mathematician, occultist, and friend of Queen Elizabeth I has never been made clear. The assumption should be that in some way Kelly and Dee had much in common at a level of sound reason. Kelly had a gift of clairvoyance and sometimes saw projected visions. The vision of the foursquare castle, which is preserved on an engraved gold plate in the British Museum, is a typically sound vision of a person who has become aware of the inner strength of his own personality. It is a symbol of unity seen on the path toward integration. We also find a psycho-logical motive in the agreement to share their wives which was reached by Kelly and Dee. They were integrating their *anima* concepts at the same time. It may have expressed the alchemical ideas of the *Soror Mystica* and it may well have been that this was the reason behind the overt drawing up of an agreement. What might have had a true and important psychological content for them resulted, however, in trouble on emotional grounds.

It must be noted that this occurred towards the end of the alchemical experiments, after Dee and Kelly had been working without success from 1583 to 1587. They had gone with Count Albert Laski to Cracow, and then visited the Emperor Rudolf II in his castle in Prague. It was the Emperor who encouraged them to continue on their way to Poland. But he was interested in occultism and may have been the means whereby the travellers obtained a Mexican black mirror which was known to have been among Dee's appa-ratus in later times, and is still in England. It appears that the relationship between John Dee and the Emperor was friendly and they were in contact on the level of scholarly students. In the case of Kelly it was different. On a second visit to Prague he was imprisoned by the Emperor, and on his release was seized again and died in an attempt to escape. This was definitely in the cause of alchemy, but not through the manufacture of the Stone (or rather the red powder).

Kelly claimed to have found the red powder through a revelation which led him to Glastonbury where he found a deposit of the wonderful sub-stance. It was revealed to him that it had been hidden by Saint Dunstan and so had remained intact for some six centuries before Kelly's discovery. Transmutations through its use gave no gain in substance but changed weight for weight, or sometimes a little less. A piece of copper cut from a warming pan was changed to gold, and the piece of gold and the pan were sent to Queen Elizabeth I. They may or may not have been genuine. In the end the denunciations of the Papal authorities led to Kelly's detention. This suggests that there was some suspicion of heresy. However, in Kelly's book on alchemy there is little really workable information, merely the old story put forward with much good sense and intelligence. One wonders again if there was any 'time-stepping' which brought the powder into Kelly's possession, and if he was more genuine than was believed at the time. It is perfectly clear that the ancient alchemy was not successfully performed by Kelly or Dee, for neither claimed to have made the Stone. It was found by occult means, and used in accordance with an occult tradition.

John Dee was primarily a mathematician and philosopher, and Kelly was a trance medium of considerable power. Their involvement with alchemy led them on a mission which may have had many diplomatic undertones. That it brought them direct to Prague was not surprising. The Emperor Rudolf II was deeply involved in alchemical and magical studies; indeed he became so fascinated by them that he withdrew from many of his official duties for the sake of the hidden knowledge.

In sixteenth-century Prague there was always a welcome for the travelling scholar. The presence of the Emperor who was more the premier occultist of Europe than an active ruler, attracted many magicians, philosophers and alchemists. The local specialists had their own street. (It now contains many laboratories which are preserved as a national museum.) Here many tests were made, not entirely without success if one credits the more authentic tales. But many an alchemist was convicted of fraud and imprisoned at the pleasure of the Emperor. The whole matter seems to have had a capricious aspect, and it is doubtful if the Emperor Rudolf was entirely sane. The conflict between imperial power and the wisdom teachings of his favourite philosophers would have ensured that he suffered an intense personality problem.

Outside the court in Prague there was a mounting strain of religious opinions which was soon to develop into the atrocious Thirty Years' War. In the East the Turks were consolidating their power. One can see that there was no means of escaping the anxieties of the time. It is true the war with the Turks led to a kind of agreement which relieved the Hapsburgs of paying tribute for a part of Hungary, although the Turks were victors in battle; but on the whole this frontier was in a state of uneasy peace. The balance of forces left Europe itself divided three ways by religion, with Islam, Protestantism and Catholicism facing an uncertain future in a world of primarily political values.

The philosophers were having a very uncertain time. In France the Age of Reason was dawning with a new tolerance after the dreadful pogrom against the Huguenots. In the states of Germany the division of religion was leading up to a reign of terror. Everything was in dispute. The most valuable contribution to philosophy in this period was probably the work of Khunrath in Germany.

In a time of struggle and uncertainty he developed a philosophical approach to alchemy. His book *Amphitheatrum Sapientiae*, of 1602, published at Magdeburg begins with a series of pictures which illustrate his ideas. They progress from the rock, which is inscribed with the text of the *Tabula Smaragdina*, to the standpoint of the philosophers by the waters of truth in which they counter the Devil's brood of falsehood and luxuriousness. Then the path moves on to the search of the wise for the entrance to the way of knowledge, which proves to be an ascent into a dark cavern leading towards a distant light. This in turn leads to the inner fortress, a seven-angled citadel, in which, through a narrow gateway of good works, the adept is led to the place of the sun and moon, and the fire at the foot of the mountain of God.

The whole of alchemy was about to change. The path of projection into chemical apparatus was about to become a theoretical study leading to understanding of the soul in its relationship to God. Yet on the way many other approaches were tried; we shall now study these in their seventeenth-century manifestations.

# 8

# SOLIFICATION

The seventeenth century was a period of turmoil and resettlement in Europe. Eastern Europe was re-awakening and the Turkish power began to retreat at last. Central Europe suffered the terrible Thirty Years' War; and new states were established as great powers. The struggles and reorganization extended through France and also through Britain where there was civil war, and the dreadful massacres of the Irish people. Occultism flourished in such an atmosphere, for people lived in fear and were anxious to know the future. Kings sought out alchemists who would make gold for them, and some claimed success. The whole period was one of unhappiness at first followed by a gradual recovery. The changed aspects of alchemy already evident in the previous century were intensified by reason of the social changes.

At this point it is wise to remember that alchemy never existed alone. The world was full of occult studies and magical activity. These varied from attempts to see into the future by simple divination, to esoteric religious developments such as those associated with the Anabaptists. Some systems had a kind of philosophical background. At the level of simple nature worship were the witch covens of remote country districts; these had little contact with the attempts of wise necromancers in the towns to raise spirits to advise their clients. Astrologers and seers were busy everywhere, and advised princes, often with some good effect. Thus the alchemist was not a lonely phenomenon. From the state's point of view he was a possible source of cheap bullion. From the spiritual point of view he was a teacher, one among those who interpreted the Bible in their own way, and was suspected of secret dark heresies. Life was not easy for such men. In fact the stronger characters were the survivors. The puffers failed and most of the simple charlatans disappeared. Some of the puffers became very important chemists, but they were the few. Of the others, the philosophers became more theoretical and less chemical.

The alchemist of medieval times was gone from his cell. His books remained to lead others, but they were used in a way he hardly imagined. The true philosophical alchemists thought of them as allegories and, although they performed the actions as a ritual, few of them saw more in the work than an illustration of a theory. However, they still provided a valuable experience, and made the mysteries more comprehensible. But the new and more materialistic mind classified the substances and appearances into a story in which the lions, dragons and doves fulfilled a dramatic purpose. It was this kind of book, with beautiful illustrations, which could be printed and obtain a ready market. Were secrets revealed too widely? Hardly, since they were not quite the secrets of the previous age, and in any case there was already so wide a range of occult literature available to those who were able to read that there was good reason for the more thoughtful alchemical works to be published.

The educated who encouraged alchemists at the beginning of the century had believed in the general philosophy of the books available. They dealt with a number of practitioners of the art, almost all of whom were beneficiaries of some adept who had originally found or prepared the Stone. One is an account of the experiences of Sendivogius who had a supply of powder which he found he could not reproduce by any method he tried. He had obtained this powder from Alexander Seton, a Scottish alchemist of the beginning of the century. How Seton had discovered the powder is not known; he only said that he was sent to prove the truth of alchemy. From time to time he had made a public transmutation before specialists, and always changed weight for weight, lead for gold. He was always able to get away after the demonstration and would mysteriously appear at some other place. Finally, after being captured by the Elector of Saxony, Christian II, Seton was tortured to extract the knowledge from him. He was rescued by Sendivogius, a Moravian gentleman, who bribed the jailers. When Seton died of his injuries shortly afterwards, he bequeathed some of his powder to Sendivogius.

At first Sendivogius failed miserably, and even though he had the advice of Seton's widow he made little progress. Then at last he found how to use Seton's powder properly. He made some demonstration transmutations, and became famous. Next he went, at the Emperor Rudolf's command, to Prague. Rudolf had seen so many charlatans that he commanded the usual test to be made before him. No doubt Michael Sendivogius was then in grave danger of spending his remaining years in a dungeon, but he had the temerity to ask the Emperor to follow his instructions and make the test himself. It was successful. After this Sendivogius was given an appointment at court, where he made some other transmutations for the Emperor. However, he was apparently of the true alchemical frame of mind since he conducted himself modestly and sought no special favours in that greedy world. Later when on a journey he was entertained by the Duke of Württemberg. A false story that the Duke was going to arrest and torture him sent the alchemist away. It is suspected that the duke plotted with his Swabian barber to 'arrange' a rescue for the alchemist. Sendivogius paid his rescuer, and later found that the hiding place of his treasured powder had been found and almost everything was stolen.

Neither the barber of Nedlingen who had taken so much trouble to convince Sendivogius that he was in danger of being tortured by the Duke, nor the Duke himself seems to have derived much benefit from their conniving. Eventually Sendivogius appealed to the Emperor who ordered the restoration of the stolen property, but the powder was never found. The Duke, to protect himself, had to hang the barber. The Swabians made one of their customary joking rhymes about the affair, and went on living under a Duke who seems to have had no alchemical gold for all his trouble and trickery.

Without the powder the alchemist could not operate, and he was quite unable to make any more. In the end it was expedient for him to travel; and some years later he was heard of as a quack doctor selling various nostrums in Poland, where he died in poverty.

The strange powder appears to have worked only when in the hands of an adept, for the Emperor was as skilled as either Seton or Sendivogius. But the Swabian alchemists do not appear to have obtained any profit from their stolen transmutation powder. The whole thing could have been done by a trick rather like that described two centuries earlier by Chaucer, but the amounts were checked by goldsmiths, and the test performed by an experienced Emperor who knew all the science of his day and who had had so many false alchemists tortured or imprisoned that we must assume that in honouring Sendivogius he gave a very definite approval to the results achieved by Seton's powder. The powder was administered in small amounts, either in a pill of wax or in a screw of yellow paper. It was not heavy enough to account for the weight of the transmutation. It was not fulminate of mercury since in its travels it had plenty of rough handling. If there was trickery it was of the most unusual skill. One does not have to assume trickery because the results are incomprehensible to our modern knowledge of the world of nature, but the whole thing seems quite impossible. Again we have a time-travelling story but only in the case of Seton who was able to get away somewhat mysteriously after his

*Folio 24 from Trismosin's* Splendor Solis

demonstrations, until the last imprisonment. What power had he lost? How did he travel from one place to another in such mystery? One either has to consider the case not proven or to assume really wonderful trickery of the quality displayed by so skilled a performer as Houdini.

But for the few who performed a transmutation of base metals to gold, there were very many who tried and failed, and still more who found it an easy way to trick people out of real money and so aid their own disappearance. How was it done? Or wasn't it ever done?

When the Emperor Rudolf II died his treasury contained four tons of gold and three tons of silver, all in neat small ingots, and it was all genuine metal apparently. Was this the last of the treasure from the Hapsburg spoils of Mexico and Peru? They had plenty of gold coming in only three generations before Rudolf. Or was it, as rumoured, alchemical gold? It is said that quantities of grey powder were found with it, but trials failed to make any transmutations. Perhaps, if this was also from America, it was grey platinum grains from the mountains of New Granada where the Indians used platinum for making fishhooks! There can be no clear answer; the equation has too many frail human elements in its composition.

One finds several curious stories in the mid-seventeenth century about the English experimenter Sir Kenelm Digby, who, particularly in his student days and later during his exile in France, took a great interest in alchemy. He was a natural magician and performed several unexplained cures, at a distance, by putting powders, usually common vitriol, on a cloth which had previously come from the diseased place. It all savours of faith healing and extra-sensory perception. The great man was one of those brilliant people who simply cannot be contained in any frame of reference. He scandalised his friends, worked hard to earn himself the character of a charlatan and did many things with such a charm of manner that all who saw believed. He maintained in one document that by using silver amalgamated with mercury and mixed with mercuric oxide, during a long process of at least three weeks, one could prepare a substance which, when fused with borax, would yield a yellow powder. This could be reheated to yield the original silver and an amount of gold equal to the mercury in the original amalgam. This sounds very like an early alchemical experiment of the type of the classical world, but it does not make sense and cannot be repeated to give any result of value. This extraordinary nobleman was so fantastic a person that he has all the mysterious charm of Harlequin. One sees a strongly marked mercurial streak in him. He was not normally of the quiet sobriety of the alchemist, but neither was he one to avoid the serious aspects of prayer and compassion for others. Probably his alchemy was more of an academic than practical nature, coming from much reading of authorities and less experiment. One of his instructors and companions in College days was Johannes Hunyades, a Hungarian who made a transmutation in Bohemia in the presence of Dr Arthur Dee, the son of John Dee; the contest between them does perhaps suggest a more systematic aim in Digby's work than one realizes. This event must have taken place before the death of Arthur Dee in 1651.

In 1661 Robert Boyle, the great scientific chemist, published his book *The Sceptical Chymist*, which, by returning to a proper use of the Greek 'element' as a name for the ultimate substances which could not be separated or broken up in any chemical experiment, disposed of the old philosophical idea of the Four Elements. We now define all our chemical elements on the principles suggested by Boyle. Earth, Air, Fire and Water have no particular meaning for us, except as poetic ideas. They are really conceptions of quality and roughly equivalent to our classificatory system of solid, liquid, and gaseous states. Fire has become an incandescent state of gaseous matter.

The appearance of a more scientific approach to the nature of the material world did not destroy belief in the possibility of transmutation of one element into another, although this is really a contradiction in terms. This was not rationalized for three centuries, when the knowledge of the internal complex structure of the atoms of chemical elements made another kind of transmutation possible, though terribly unprofitable.

The difference of thought was not quite so real as one might imagine. The alchemists had become more and more a group of specialists in search of a vision. It was still apparent to them that their 'elements' had an inner meaning which was quite apart from the material composition of the substances concerned. They were much less concerned with real experiments and became more and more interested in the philosophical approach to the inner spiritual nature of the universe. In fact they were already well on the way to becoming a small group of esoteric philosophers who expected that their experiments would be conditioned by their own personal qualities. The experimenter performed the work done within his own soul, and the outward evidence, the transmutation of metals, was simply material proof of an immaterial progress. It was against the principles of the true alchemist to make gold for his own benefit. He should be above such considerations as profitability or the aquisition of wealth for personal aggrandisement. In fact he was feeling more and more clearly that the power of transmutation came from God and was given only to the adept who had achieved high spiritual progress. Sir Kenelm Digby, in his *Lucerna Salis*, makes it very clear that the alchemist can only progress through earnest prayer, and that if he departs from this course God will bring about obstacles to the work, or even direct it to a complete catastrophe.

Meanwhile the tragedies of Europe in this period were making ordinary ideas about religion and philosophy highly suspect. The thinking man could not contemplate the brutalities of the religious wars without being forced to look for some path of basic understanding which would give him a more stable view of the universe and the nature of God. Naturally anyone who realized that the political systems of the period were usually wrong, and that the religious beliefs of both the old Church and the Reformers were distorted, would be in danger. Religious persecution reached an almost unbelievable level of brutality in the seventeenth century of the Christian era. In Germany, Ireland and Switzerland, armies were on the move and whole populations were subjected to pillage and massacre. In such a world the poor shoemaker's son Jakob Boehme and the respected teacher Heinrich Khunrath were the most important among many people who found an answer to the dilemma. They were both influenced by ideas of the alchemists, Khunrath directly as an experimenter, Boehme partly by a deep insight into the world of nature and partly from the diffusion of alchemical ideas throughout Europe.

None of the new philosophical alchemists was equipped to follow the paths of rationalization of chemical science which was being followed in England, and yet their work was not neglected as a basic philosophy by the scientists. Sir Isaac Newton was very interested in Boehme's teaching, but did not turn his path of serious studies on the material plane into part of his philosophical teaching. He was probably thinking in the classical way about the essential unity of all physical and mechanical laws, and so gained a wider understanding of reality.

It was precisely at this time, when much of alchemical teaching was available to a wide public, that the numbers of false gold-makers fell off. The hordes of these scoundrels and dupes which characterized the fifteenth and sixteenth centuries were reduced to the status of a few charlatans and confidence tricksters. The reason for the change is difficult to assess. It was perhaps partly owing to the diffusion of knowledge among the educated people which meant that the counterfeiter was obliged to show an expensively equipped laboratory. Besides this, the new social structure made access to the real rulers of Europe, who needed money, much more difficult. Merchants might be induced to invest in a South Sea Bubble, but one hears nothing of them financing an alchemist.

The loss to alchemy was probably not very great. The adepts were fewer and much more secretive. They were much more likely to be found among serious elders discussing the nature of the salvation of mankind, than in a laboratory. No doubt there was compassion for the desperate straits of the surviving puffers who, seeking for gold, lost all their wealth and gained only ridicule, but the adepts felt themselves to be above such practices. They saw that the puffers were forging their own failure through having the wrong objects of desire. The process was so much tied up with psychological conditions that it was axiomatic that the wrong man got the wrong results.

As the century drew to its close the world's attitude to the alchemists changed. They were seen as dreamers or just harmless eccentric philosophers. The whole of the spagiric art was neglected. Science and theology held equal sway as two branches of learning about the universe.

From this period comes the most authentic of all accounts of the transmutation, by Helvetius (Johann Friedrich Schweitzer) who encountered an adept in 1666. The visitor was secretive, and possessed a rich treasure of which he was willing on a second visit to give a very small grain. A stolen smear of the material proved useless but the adept gave instruction in the proper procedure and departed. He did not reappear as promised. When Helvetius was prompted by his wife to make a trial of his grain of material, the experiment succeeded. If it has been a sequence of dreams, it would show that Helvetius was advancing pyschologically to a high degree of individuation and was becoming aware of a further step. But the visitor appeared to be a real person and the gold-making was witnessed by friends. While the gold was still hot it was assayed by an independent goldsmith, and that same morning it was tested by the city authorities.

The time and place are given: 27 December 1666 at the Hague. The amount transmuted was a little over half an ounce of lead, and the gold was valued by a professional goldsmith at a rate of fifty florins an ounce, which in those days was a very good price. Helvetius had no need of publicity, and since he prepared the lead in his own crucible before the test there was no possibility of its being anything but lead. The tiny grain of the Stone was put into wax by Helvetius's wife in his presence. All the lead was transmuted, and tested. It was not gilded nor was there any addition of a pill of gold. The work was done quite rapidly in a crucible heated on an open fire, not in closed vessels. The news of the strange transmutation brought visitors of note to the laboratory; but they already knew Helvetius, and he gained nothing beyond a few florins, if he had wanted them, from the experiment. He literally had no reason for deception. Yet he acted out a kind of dream which was reality.

At the time Helvetius was 41, and he assessed the age of his visitor as about 43 or 44. The visitor seemed unremarkable; Helvetius thought he came from

North Holland. He notes that he came into his inner study with shoes still covered with mud and snow, but says that it was the custom to do so in Holland at that time. (Did he anticipate a thought that the stranger had 'apported' to his laboratory?). The visitor was dressed in 'plebeian' clothes, was of average height (5' 8"?) with a small pale face, lank black hair and no beard. He was polite and gentle although he spoke with authority. He mentioned that he had wished to visit Helvetius in company with a friend, because he had read the article which the scientist had written about the foolish statements in one of Sir Kenelm Digby's accounts of transmutation. He wished to demonstrate a universal medicine to Helvetius. He admitted that he had been a brass-founder, and that he had learned from a friend how to extract the universal medicine from metal through the use of fire. (At this point it seems that his name was Elias, or was Helvetius comparing him to Elias?).

The stranger, after a discussion about alchemical books, took an ivory box from a pouch he carried in his bosom. In it he had three walnut-sized lumps of a very heavy substance, of an amber colour, which still had metallic scales, from a crucible, on them. He told Helvetius of the many powers of this substance in healing and transmuting, and claimed that in his pouch there was enough to transmute about twenty tons of gold. Helvetius asked why the substance was yellow and not red like a ruby as the books described; he was simply told that it was in itself the true substance. Next he asked if he might have a little of the substance but the stranger answered in these words:

O, no, no! This is not lawful though thou wouldst give me as many ducats in gold as would fill this room, *not for the value of the matter but for some particular consequences not lawful to divulge*, nay, if it were possible that fire could be burnt of fire, I would rather at this instant cast all this substance into the fiercest flames.

However, he decided to be kind to Helvetius and asked him to take him to a room where they could not be observed. He was taken to the best furnished room at the back of the house. (It was here that Helvetius noticed the snow and mud on his shoes.) Then he showed Helvetius five golden medals which he wore under his shirt. They were hanging on green silk ribbons. Each one had an inscription which Helvetius was allowed to copy down. These inscriptions were religious in nature, and in spite of the green ribbon (emblem of witchcraft and nature magic), the stranger lost something of the demonic aspect he displayed in the front room. The inscriptions were as follows:

Holy Holy Holy
is the Lord our God
The Universe is full
of His glory.

Sign LEO. Sign LIBRA.

Jehovah's
Wonderful and Miraculous
Wisdom
in the Catholic Book
of Nature
I was made the
26 August 1666.

Signs: SOL  MERCURIUS  LUNA
God, Nature and
the Spagiric Art
make nothing
in vain.

Holy, Sacred Spirit!
Halleluia Halleluia Halleluia
Avaunt Satan
Speak not of God without
Light.
Amen.

To the Eternal
Invisible, Triune, Thrice
Holy, and only wise God,
the Governor and
Preserver,
be praise now and ever.

This is probably not the right order: it is more comprehensible if on both the upper and the lower pair we read the right-hand inscription first.

After this display the stranger told how he in turn had been visited by a curious looking stranger who had taught him all he knew about the medicines of the day and showed him how to prepare elixirs. He also taught how to make jewels of great beauty (paste?), and then he demonstrated transmutation both to silver and then to gold. Helvetius was apparently fascinated and asked for some practical information. However, the stranger dismissed himself, saying that he would return in three weeks.

At this point we could look at the account and treat it as a dream record. The stranger was perhaps the shadow aspect of Helvetius himself. The questioning of his doubts and the answer by showing the symbols as well as verbal assertion, might reflect a real struggle going on in his personality because of the mysteries which he was disputing, particularly about the transmuting powder of Kenelm Digby. He has reassured himself, in a dream, that his visitor comes from the real outer world with snow on his boots. In the inner *mandala* (the shape of the room) the story is told and there is an affirmation, made doubly sure by the arrangement of medals on the chest of the stranger. The central medal has the message: the symbols of Sun, Moon and Mercury with the announcement that God, Nature and the Spagiric Art make nothing in vain. The problem would thus be solved, for the dreamer has realized that in his heart he knows the process to be true. The stranger furthermore goes on to give his version of a similar experience which happened to him, and his account of his studies is a kind of promise that Helvetius should also prosper in the studies commenced with this vision.

But on the appointed day the stranger returned to Helvetius's house in the Hague. The stranger and Helvetius walked outdoors this time in a friendly discussion. The stranger talked first about religious matters, but Helvetius turned the conversation to a discussion of workshop practice in the alchemical attempt at transmutation of metals. He told the stranger how he had prepared his laboratory just as he had heard at the first meeting, and indeed he had been promised some further instruction. 'Yea, true,' was the reply, 'But I promised to teach thee at my return with this proviso: *if it were not forbidden.*'

Thereupon the scientist, realizing that to continue the discussion would be useless, begged a small portion of the marvellous stone. The stranger, after much thought, gave him a small piece, as small as a rape-seed, and said: 'Receive this small parcel of the greatest treasure in the world which truly few kings or princes have ever known or seen.' It was so small that Helvetius protested that it could hardly change even four grains of metal to gold. But the stranger took it back, halved it, and threw the other half in the fire. (Note that at the previous meeting he suggested it was indestructible by fire.) He wrapped the remaining half in blue paper and gave it to Helvetius saying, 'It is yet sufficient for thee.' Helvetius protested but only got the reply: 'If thou canst not manage this; yet for its great proportion for so small a quantity of lead, then put into the crucible two drachms or half an ounce, or a little more of the lead; for there ought to be no more lead put in the crucible than the medicine can work upon, and transmute.'

It was then that Helvetius confessed that at the first meeting he had scraped one of the stones with his nail. He had cleaned the material on to a piece of paper and put this infinitesimal amount of the substance into a crucible of lead. The result was an explosion. Most of the lead blew away and the remainder turned into 'a mere glassy earth'. (This sounds like a kind of lead glaze used by potters at that time.) However, the stranger advised him further:

Thou art more dexterous to commit theft than to apply thy Tincture: for if thou hadst only wrapped up thy stolen prey in yellow wax, to preserve it from the arising fumes of lead, it would have penetrated to the bottom of the lead, and transmuted it to gold; but having cast it into the fumes, partly by the violence of the vaporous fumes and partly by the sympathetic alliance, it carried thy medicine quite away: For gold, silver, quick-silver, and the like metals are corrupted and turn brittle like to glass by the vapours of lead.

Helvetius brought the crucible, and the stranger perceived a most beautiful saffron-like tincture on the sides. We are not told whether Helvetius had noticed it before.

This is the first part of the day's conversation. One notices that the precious substance was first wrapped in blue paper (the unconscious mind?) and that its rash use would only result in frustration; though it is not said to have been a result of a moral sanction against theft. In the correct process it had to be wrapped in yellow wax, presumably to protect it as it sank into the fiery torment of the molten lead. But we note that yellow suggests the presence of the *anima* image, Helvetius's feminine aspect. The whole business may be an allegory though it is shown under a very ordinary guise.

The second part of the conversation at the second visit of the stranger followed the importuning by Helvetius for more laboratory information and details of the materials used. He was rewarded by a fascinating series of parables which all had some reference to alchemy and yet all of which are unclear.

My friend, thou art too curious to know all things in an instant, yet I will discover so much; that neither the great charge nor length of time, can discourage any; for as for the matter out of which our magistery is made, I would have thee know that there are only two metals and minerals, out of which it is prepared; but in regard the sulphur of philosophers is much more plentiful and abundant in the minerals; therefore it is made out of the minerals.

Then Helvetius asked what the menstruum (solvent or flux) used by the alchemists was.

He answered that the menstruum was a heavenly salt, or of heavenly virtue, by whose benefit only the wise men dissolve the earthly metallic body, and by such a solution is easily and instantly brought forth the most noble elixir of philosophers. But in a crucible is all the operation done and performed, from the beginning to the very end, in an open fire, and all the whole work is no longer from the very first to last than four days, and the whole work is no more charge than three florins; and further neither the mineral, out of which, nor the salt by which it was performed, was of any great price.

# The Seventeenth Century: Comment and Illustration

In the seventeenth century the alchemist was often a victim of derision. Here he is represented as a fanatic obsessed with the idea of making gold, while he and his family live in appalling poverty

VPERTATEM ALI₉ FVGIT, AST HIC ADVOCAT IPSAM

*Overleaf:* An alchemical laboratory *c.* 1650

ELIAS ASHMOLE.

Alchemical horoscopes
with planetary data on a
basic framework. A page
from Thomas Norton's
*Ordinall of Alchimy*, part of
Ashmole's *Theatrum
Chemicum Britannicum*

The title-page from Ashmole's
*Theatrum Chemicum Britannicum*

*THEATRVM CHEMICVM*
**BRITANNICVM.**
CONTAINING
Severall Poeticall Pieces of our Famous
*English Philosophers*, who have written
the *Hermetique Mysteries* in their owne
Ancient Language.

Faithfully Collected into one **Volume**,
with Annotations thereon,
*By* ELIAS ASHMOLE, *Esq.*
*Qui est Mercuriophilus Anglicus.*

THE FIRST PART.

*Serpens et Bufo gradiens sup terrâ, Aquila
volans, est nostrū Magisteriū.*

LONDON,
Printed by *J. Grismond* for NATH: BROOKE, at the
Angel in *Cornhill.* MDCLII.

*Opposite:* A portrait of Elias Ashmole
(1617–92) from the frontispiece of his
*Theatrum Chemicum Britannicum*. He was
a Mercurian born under Gemini

The alchemist and his
assistant in their laboratory

The adept in his laboratory:
separation and conjunction
are under his control

The process in the
laboratory inspired by the
sages of the past—Geber,
Arnold of Villanova,
Rayyi and Hermes
Trismegistus

The secret of the alchemist
is a gift from God which is
passed down from master
to pupil

DRACO non moritur, nisi cum fratre & forore sua inter-
ficiatur, qui sunt Sol & Luna.

EPIGRAMMA XXV.

Exigua est non artis opus stravisse Draconem
Funere, ne serpat mox redivivus humo.
Frater & ipsa soror juncti simul illius ora
Fuste premunt, nec res fert aliena necem.
Phœbus ei frater, soror est at Cynthia, Python
Illâ, ast Orion hac cecidêre manu.

O₃            In

Two pages from Michael Maier's
*Secretioris Naturae Secretorum Scrutinium
Chymicum*, published in Frankfurt in
1687

The brother-sister pair defeat the
dragon in their guise as sun and
moon

EMBLEMA XXIX.  *De secretis Natura.*
Ut Salamandra vivit igne sic lapis:

EPIGRAMMA XXIX.

Egit in ardenti Salamandra potentior igne,
Nec Vulcane tuas æstimat illa minas:
Sic quoque non flammarum incendia sæva recusat,
Qui fuit assiduo natus in igne Lapis.
Illa rigens æstus extinguit, liberáque exit,
At calet hic, similis quem calor inde juvat.

Q₃

The salamander, like the
philosopher's stone, lives in the fire

When Helvetius objected that the philosophers said that the work took from seven to nine months he replied:

Their writings are only to be understood by the true adeptists; wherefore concerning time they would write nothing certain: Nay, without the communication of a true adept Philosopher, not one student can find the way to prepare this great magistery, for which cause I warn and charge thee (as a friend) not to fling away thy money and goods to hunt out this art; for thou shalt never find it.

Again Helvetius suggested that perhaps he could be given a foundation from which he could discover further for himself. The stranger replied:

In this art 'tis quite otherwise; for unless thou knowest the thing from the head to the heel, from the eggs to the apples; that is, from the very beginning to the very end, thou knowest nothing; and though I have told thee enough, yet thou knowest not how the philosophers do make, and break open the glassy seal of Hermes, in which the Sun sends forth a great splendour with his marvellous coloured metallic rayes, and in which looking glass the eyes of Narcissus behold the transmutable metals, for out of those rays the true adept philosophers gather their fire; by whose help the volatile metals may be fixed into the most permanent metals, either gold or silver.

But enough at present; for I intend (God willing) once more tomorrow at the ninth hour (as I said) to meet, and discourse further on this philosophical subject, and shall show you the manner of projection.

But after a friendly leave taking the adept went off and never came to Helvetius again. This is not surprising since he had already given two warnings that he was not allowed to give more information. In fact to judge from the first utterances he had already transgressed some unspecified boundary of knowledge.

Dreams? The whole series of incidents could be detailed waking visions, which fit into a very clear pattern. Helvetius was well acquainted with the literature of the subject, and was already a man of developed personality. All could have been psychologically right. The story might have been an unconscious fabrication, *but* . . .

The following night his wife asked Helvetius to test the grain of the precious transmutant. He had the fire lit, he said, so at least one laboratory assistant was present; and at the conclusion of the transmutation he mentions that all present were amazed, implying that there were several witnesses. Then came the two tests first by the goldsmith and second by the assay officers. Lead had been transmuted to gold, and very pure gold at that.

Thus almost the last authenticated transmutation is one of the most clearly described, by an authority of really high scientific standing. Already alchemy is dying, but it leaves this first-class mystery, to make sure that it cannot pass from the human mind.

In the late seventeenth and throughout the eighteenth centuries the stories continue, but transmutations are fewer and less public. The philosophers turn more and more to studies of alchemical import which deal with the world of religion and relate the mysterious routines of the alchemist to the development of the soul.

# 9

# NIGREDO

The beginning of the eighteenth century was marked by quite a spate of gold medals produced by alchemists for Heads of State. There were several eye-witnesses who failed to detect forgery, but there are even more accounts of tricksters and false alchemists who managed to show a little gold produced in unusual circumstances, and then extracted far more by promising huge quantities of the Philosopher's Stone to any gullible prince who paid out from the Treasury for the privilege. Usually the alchemist managed to decamp. Sometimes he was caught and thrown into an uncomfortable dungeon to rot.

These experiments in transmutation, even the successful ones, were made before a limited but often uninformed circle. The princes and their ministers may have been believers, and perhaps not even very greedy for gold, but they were not adepts. There was no great element of philosophy in the work, and its ends were the benefit of state organization and not of human care for suffering individuals. The whole thing was contrary to the teaching of the earlier alchemists. Gold-making for public advancement was one thing; the philosophical preparation of the individual before attempting transmutation was something quite different. In the later days of the eighteenth century there were a few remarkable individuals who did not claim to be alchemists, but who in the course of their occult studies were able to enrich themselves and their friends.

The two most famous were the Comte de St Germain, and Cagliostro. Each travelled with a beautiful lady who was his wife; each had apparently inexhaustible funds during the height of his career. It is however more often said that these funds came through the organization of a secret society of occultists which included many very rich subscribers rather than that the Philosopher's Stone was involved. They never divulged any alchemical recipes, or rituals. St Germain's book, *The Thrice Holy Trinosophie*, now preserved at Troyes, has much Hermetic material, and some pictures of ritual, which really belong to philosophical types of occultism, but are given a Hermetic framework because of the newly aroused enthusiasm for Egypt derived from Napoleon's expedition. The cults of Thoth, who was rightly regarded as a form of Hermes Trismegistus, were encouraged and developed their characteristic rituals before the hieroglyphic writing was deciphered. The path cannot have been lost, but it was certainly allowed to become hidden.

Materials for transmutation seem to have differed widely and the chemical preparation for the making of the Stone was reduced to the minimum. This was implicit in much alchemical literature, since the emphasis, in the later days of the art, was on its simplicity. The true adept was believed to be enlightened to the extent that a simple material and a few operations with the furnace were all that was necessary.

A curious example was Manuel Caetano who, at the beginning of the century, was acclaimed by some witnesses as the master of alchemical knowledge, and in other places was found to be a fraud and an imposter. He was at once a goldsmith and a skilled practitioner of legerdemain. Thus nothing is to be expected of him. In Spain and in Vienna he was successful, even performing before the court. In Brussels he was imprisoned for six years for attempting to escape with coins worth in today's currency about £30,000. In the end he was arrested after some trickery in Berlin, escaped and was recaptured. In 1709 the Prussian king decided to make him a brilliant example for all such tricksters. Caetano was hanged in a golden cloak on a gilded gallows, swinging quietly and glittering in the wind. Perhaps other kings who had been fooled felt happier at this picturesque spectacle.

Yet at the same time in Sweden General Paykhull won a reprieve from a sentence of death by making a transmutation before King Charles XII. He said he received the mastery from a Pole, who had it from a priest from Carinthia. Before credible witnesses a mass of mixed metals was melted, and Paykhull added his elixir wrapped in a piece of lead. It produced metal for 147 golden ducats. A medal was cast and dated Stockholm 1706. Here there seems rather less chance of deception than in most cases, and the gold remains; nevertheless the details do not reach the standards of the Helvetius story of forty years earlier. The main interest is that the material is said to have come originally from an adept who was a priest in a far-off land. In this there is an echo of the medieval tradition.

Of course in this century, and even to modern times, the more ancient traditions of Arabian alchemy continued in the Islamic world; but they continued mainly as a religious tradition, and did not claim to produce great quantities of gold. The alchemists were more concerned to demonstrate the ancient views of the relationship between the soul and the material world. The thought was in consonance with Islam. Only in a few places were there adepts who saw the occult mysteries which were enshrined in alchemical tradition. So while the ancient tradition persisted in a small way mostly in North Africa, the development and change went on in the violently altering society in Europe. From this one can deduce that even secretive groups like alchemists were subject to change under the pressure of altering social structure.

It was the general change in the social structure from medieval patterns through to the new commercial world of large acquisitive monarchies, which divided alchemy. The puffers and their descendants, even the successful ones, were diverted into the apparatus of state. They were expected to make gold available with more certainty than speculative trading enterprises. Usually they failed. This had to be so because if there were any truth in the ancient doctrine that the state of soul of the worker was part of the Work, these men had no chance. They were simply not the right kind of people. Most philosophers had, on the other hand, left the orthodox faiths and were exploring new ways of finding a transcendental knowledge of God and His created world. The traditions of the alchemists were ready for study even when they found the ideas stemming from a spiritual illumination which was not due to conscious reasoning. Only a few of them went through the ancient experimental rituals. The idea was to expound to themselves the astrological, chemical and spiritual ideas of alchemy. But probably most students had substituted theoretical study for experimental alchemy.

The last of the officially sponsored tests of gold-making ended in tragedy, the suicide of James Price, MA, MD, of Stoke D'Abernon in Surrey. Price had inherited a considerable fortune and bought a house at Stoke, where he performed several experiments in pursuit of his personal interest in chemistry. This led him to alchemical experiments which yielded startling results. Price issued a pamphlet about transmutation, but as usual it really gave no details, and was written in confusing terms. The mistake was probably in issuing a pamphlet at all, and, of course, in trying to achieve personal fame. However, the pamphlet aroused interest and Price invited a group of the social élite of the day, including Lord Palmerston, to witness transmutations. They saw, but did not make any scientific check, that Price used a white powder, of which he was unwilling to give the formula.

Price took the powder and fifty times its weight of mercury, mixed them with borax and nitre, and heated them while stirring with an iron rod. (This should have produced quite a spectacular bubbling and fizzing.)

It was allowed to cool when all appeared of an even consistency. The cooled mass came out of the crucible as silver of the same weight as the mercury.

Again, sixty parts of mercury were added to one part of a red powder (an old friend, from medieval alchemy) and after the operation was over the ingot poured from the crucible proved to be gold. Price allowed the ingots to be assayed, and they were admitted to be pure silver and gold. Meanwhile it had not escaped the eye of the scientifically minded people of that time, that Price's pamphlets were all poppycock and would not lead to anything. Some of the more learned began to suspect that Price hardly deserved his MA degree. There was dispute, and finally a committee of the Royal Society led by Sir Joseph Banks, the botanist, insisted that Price should demonstrate transmutation before them. Price hedged and delayed, sought to obtain information from philosophic friends in Germany, and finally, when he could delay no longer, prepared a demonstration for the committee at his house in Stoke. He made no transmutation, but drank an acid poison and died before their eyes. Apparently Price was an imposter. At the Coroner's inquest he was adjudged to have been insane. The white powder was never analysed, and the whole matter was just another tragedy in the history of the advance of clear-headed modern science. Price had at least been medieval in his obscurantist tactics. Did Lord Palmerston see gold made by trans-mutation from mercury? It is all rather doubtful, and neither entirely convincing nor disproven. That, of course, is one of the maddening features of the whole alchemical record. It is not enough to say that the whole thing was impossible. It was more than improbable, and from a scientific stand-point we now know that one could not expect to perform a transmutation without a vast array of atomic and electronic gear. Yet a few eye-witness accounts lead to wonderment.

A more pleasant feature of eighteenth-century occultism was the development of the idea of the *Soror Mystica*. This feminine companion of the experimenter was really a magical or even witch-cult personality. Psycho-logically she was the equivalent of the *anima*. Practically she was a feminine companion who must not be the wife of the experimenter and in some way one with whom it was improper to have sexual relationships. So the younger alchemical experimenters could often search for the inner truth of the mystery of the development of nature and the mystical parables of the cosmos in a personal contact of the sexes. In the age of science this was not unreasonable, but it went right back to the fertility cults of Egypt. Alchemy came from the name of the black earth of the Nile, which was the source of so many living things.

Alchemists had always used a sexual symbolism in the descriptions of their work, and in some of the illustrations this was quite overt. Yet it meant no more than the illustrations to a Greek myth. In classical times it was openly understood and treated as a wonderful thing that the process of human generation was an image of the generation of the material cosmos. It never reached the totality of expression that it had in Polynesian religion, but it had a very important place in thought. However in the medieval period, both in Islamic countries and in the Christian West, the picture symbols were seen as illustrations of facts of everyday life, lifted on to a higher plane. The action of sexual unity was the action of the whole creative universe, and we find that the alchemical illustrations represent the same kind of thought as in the religious books of the same period. There are all the usual amusing little shynesses, and curious articulations of limbs. But there is no doubt that the mysteries are described on the analogy that the perfecting of the Philosopher's Stone is similar to the process of love, birth, death, rebirth, and glorification. All the powers of nature are called in, and assume the symbols and colours of the minerals and planets, but the human beings remain human throughout.

As time moves on the illustrative treatment of the process becomes more elegantly drawn and the details are put with a proper honesty in the analogy with the sexual life. The Renaissance had awakened an interest in realism but a greater sense of beauty gradually developed.

By the seventeenth century we find wood engravings which reduce the symbols to the actions of life. The king and queen are as happily united in sex as any ordinary scientist, and are marked solely by crowns as they go through their experience of life, death and rebirth followed by the perfect reunion. It is all very like what little we hear of the classical mystery religions with their exposition of the *hieros gamos*, the physical marriage between the priestess and priest for the bringing of new life to the initiates through association of ideas.

One suspects that sometimes in this later period, and in the eighteenth century, the sexual parallel of the alchemical ritual was pursued more or less secretly. This was a period of classicism and of freedom of behaviour, where intellectuals would not be outraged by this quiet enaction of the mysteries of life. Perhaps the significant fact about this aspect of the discovery of the force of life and growth was that any real enactment was performed by the philosophic alchemists who were not young. The whole thing could never have been an orgiastic coming together in the wild joy of living, but must have been a strangely ritual act with an intellectual purpose behind it. Perhaps that explains the directness and innocence of the alchemical illustrations when compared with the works of erotic art which adorned rich men's cabinets in those days.

However, the presence of eroticism in alchemical art was important, and was made more clear in the later times of the art. Even if it was never actually turned into a ritual intercourse, it served to link the process of transmutation with the nature of life. It was a good feature of alchemy in that it reinforced the adept's understanding of the essential unity between the microcosm and the macrocosm; between the forces of life in human beings and the forces of creation in the universe as a whole. They were still happy in the romantic conception that love and sex were practically identical and so their philosophy, bubbling up through the theosophical ideas of the eighteenth century, was willing to accept the idea that love was a major creative force. It might have been the equivalent of another dimension of the universe for them, rather similar to the circumambient ether of the early chemists. In fact we may be thankful that Sir Isaac Newton used the idea of *gravitas* (weight), to name his newly-discovered force linking the planets and the sun instead of the alchemical idea of a universal attraction of the nature of love.

This was another part of the separation of the different strains of thought in the alchemical system. As the age of science dawned the differences between alchemist and scientist became more and more pronounced. The linkage of words remained in some cases, but how the meanings differed! It is not surprising that the alchemical books became increasingly incomprehensible to those who tried to find reason in their deliberate contradictions and pairings of opposites.

The whole matter of the union, separation and reunion of living force was inherent in alchemy. It goes back to the earlier philosophies from which it derived, particularly to the mythology of ancient Egypt. The union of earth and sky, personified as the male earth god, Geb, and the sky goddess, Nut, is a key point for the creation of a world in which life will spring up by generation (*opposite*). It is the same as the Polynesian myth of Rangi and Papa. In other words, this idea is archetypal and must appear in all developing religions. The Egyptians had a special example before their unscientific eyes. They saw the fertile mud of the inundations spawn forth frogs and flies, weeds and flowers. Life arose more abundantly from the black earth. Thus this strand of the alchemical web was one of its earliest parts and was bound to come to prominence once again when the whole system was threatened by dissolution.

The beginning of the Age of Reason was probably the nadir of alchemy. Could any thinking person accept the curious stories of the medieval past?

*Section from the Egyptian Papyrus of Taweniu (c. 1000 BC), representing the separation of earth and sky at the Creation*

It was impossible to understand the operation of green dragons, or of the serpent devouring its own tail. The intelligentsia of the time were steeped in classical studies, but they never thought of the gods of Olympus or the enchantress, Medea, as representing the forces of nature. Science was a separate subject and the value of the classics was mainly to produce a more elegant and precise use of language. By analogy Greek words were used for chemical substances, and states of materials, with no reference to the philosophical or alchemical terms. There was no reason why the rational world of science should give credence to alchemy any more.

On the other hand there was a considerable development of a kind of philosophical magic. Studies on Mesmerism, cartomancy, and occultism flourished. They were on the fringe of the world of the alchemists, but mostly never took the turning which would lead to any inner unifying meaning. They are rather like the castle in Khunrath's ultimate diagram, where the seekers who arrive through the mysterious darkness find themselves faced with many chambers, each of which has its own fascination and its own passages linking with other chambers of thought, and yet never directly communicates with the single narrow bridge to the central truth. Sometimes the groups sought ecstatic experience in activities like those of the monks of Medmenham, who practised a good deal of black magic. Some were philosophic in a mystical way. They included the curious vigil of Sir Francis Dashwood and three companions in the tower of a church on his estate, where the meditation and occult combination of symbols was said to have released strange forces which in turn activated the French Revolution. Only very few people at this period of change seem to have understood that there was a mystery religion of which the adepts were alchemists. In fact even the adepts preferred be unrecognized.

It is instructive to note how the paths of Cagliostro and the Comte de St Germain covered central European states as well as the more sophisticated West. They travelled through an area where alchemy had its greatest public regard. Their secret ways, passing from one interested nobleman to the next, were the ways by which the Philosopher's Stone had once travelled in powder form. Their unexpected and unexplained sources of wealth may have included some gold produced by alchemists. It may, on the other hand, have been contributed by rich members of a confraternity. The whole ritual was all very dark and secret; it was gradually enshrined in the theories of 'Trinosophie', and had an Egyptian flavour inspired not by ancient tradition, but by the discoveries of Napoleon's scientists among the ruins of Memphis and Thebes. A very curious piece of accidental prophecy is to be found in *The Thrice Holy Trinosophie* where the sybil, or priestess, is dressed in high boots, no top and a short skirt. Her hair is long and worn loose. This was a deliberate device to imitate supposed Greco-Egyptian styles, but reflected some deeper current in life which was to flower more elegantly a century and a half later.

At this period there were no more alchemical charlatans of any importance. The very name of alchemist suggested a romantic and almost mythical picture of a kind of sorcerer. Yet the inner thoughts of the alchemists were independently derived from visions such as those experienced by Emanuel Swedenborg, and a little later by William Blake. Their followers realized the relationship with the ideas of such men as Freiherr, Boehme and Khunrath, who represented a more direct link with the world of alchemy.

The change was one of emphasis. The making of gold was largely abandoned. A very few wise men secretly continued the tradition, but these were in the Arab lands rather than in Europe. They were very antiquarian in their attitude. The Europeans were following the path of symbolism and meditation which led to visions. These in turn brought new experiences to the mind and prepared the soul for its transmutation by illumination from above.

The philosophic mind at the turn of the eighteenth century was realizing the teaching of the alchemists about the need for an approach to be made to God so that He would reach downwards and give illumination to the searcher. The search was less and less for the material symbols, or for a means of witnessing the mysteries in the furnaces and vessels of the laboratory. Now the human soul was to be sought out and purified through many adversities. The symbols of the planets and metals became symbols of the steps towards illumination.

We cannot say that alchemy was dead but it was transmuted. The process is explained by C. G. Jung as a reflection of the development of the human realization of the psyche. Alchemists no longer found it easy to project the drama of individuation onto the chemicals of the laboratory worker. The aim of the process was to unite the *materia prima*, the Common Unconscious which we all share to some extent, and which appears to have an almost unfathomable extension in time and space, with the personal unconscious and the little star of consciousness, so that man became infused with the light of his whole integrated personality. This was not possible for all mankind to achieve then, nor is it possible for us all now. Nevertheless, the personal aspect of the alchemical experience became more widely available to those who sought out the path, or who, in the case of Jung's patients, were forced by circumstances to make the perilous journey towards unity.

A total explanation of the facts of the alchemical experience is not yet reached, for there are other aspects, such as the material apparition of gold and silver of high quality, which in a few cases cannot be explained by any materialist hypothesis.

But out of the darkness which shrouded the subject in the nineteenth century something was bound to arise as a clarification of mysteries. The psychological aspect was not new. It is implicit in alchemy from the beginning, but it was assuming greater clarity. The hidden light which illumined the adept was growing more and more like the growth of unity in the human personality. It was again a statement of the unison between the microcosm and the macrocosm, the new translation of ideas about the 'fluid' which was believed to exist between all the particles of the universe.

# 10

# the dark journey

No one can study the work of the alchemists without acquiring a sense of their belief in the need for the repetition of actions. For each repetition of the process they expected an essentially similar result, but apparently a point was reached where a critical repetition resulted in an important change. This might have been due to infinitesimal alterations in the material within the vessel on the furnace, slightly more refined towards purity at each change. The result was apparent as a kind of intervention. At each time the opposites to be reconciled in union were the same until after a special experience they became idealized. Whether the alchemical philosophers of today expect an enlightenment of this kind in the near future seems impossible to discover.

The nineteenth century began with the philosophies associated with Swedenborg and Freiherr which contained some of the alchemical message. The visionary world of William Blake had some affinity with them, although Blake formed his own mythology as his visions developed. The majority of people at this time, however, could see absolutely no reason why civilized man should seek either to purify himself or make gold. The development of industry with its capitalization on an increasingly wide basis meant that the banker and the principal shareholder replaced the maker of gold for use by a king. The curious smugness of an age of industrial development made the investigation of the spiritual side of alchemy seem nonsensical to most people. There was difficulty enough in finding any real response to Christianity, let alone to a secretive mystery religion. The alchemical tradition in these matters meant facing and questioning one's own personal fitness to be an adept, and suffering a great deal of hard work in the process of purification.

The Romantic Movement of the early nineteenth century filled many books with fantasy. The alchemists became mysterious romantics, portrayed in the novels which gave much innocent happiness to those who could read.

Whether the books inspired anything else is doubtful. But there was at least a mild interest in occultism of many kinds, which was inspired by such novels as *Frankenstein*. It all seems far removed from the serious studies and wise discourses of secretive philosophers. But at least the growing world of European commerce had not discarded the memory of a more attractive and colourful past. An important figure in all this was the re-created Dr Faustus, now in magnificent literary form, through the great work of Goethe.

Goethe in many ways was a child of the philosophic alchemists. He studied the literature during his illness of 1768–9, and read Swedenborg and Paracelsus. His attitude to scientific work was that of one who seeks a unity in all nature. His thought in later years was very like the best of alchemic feeling about the nature of life as an ever-changing reconciliation, separation and recombination of apparently opposed forces. He believed the life within nature was truly an expression of the unified being of God. His *Stirb und werde!* was very like the alchemical idea that the *materia prima* must die and be recreated in a higher form during the process. The final version of Faust was the culmination of a process of change within the soul of the philosopher-poet. It shows the curious world of ancient occultism, its dangers and confusions, and the means of escape from its alluring pitfalls. That Faust is not the itinerant conjurer who wandered around Tübingen cadging money from students is the measure of the drama. The history of an individual expands into the drama of the great soul entrapped by a magic glamour which could only lead to disaster.

In the philosophic statement that man must look within himself to seek the way of salvation, Goethe was already following part of the mystery tradition which had come down from the ancient world, and which was to find new prominence with the development of psychology in the twentieth century.

It is clear that a few alchemists worked in obscurity and that the old laboratory procedure never totally died out, but it seems unlikely that we shall ever find out much about them. They were unknowingly bridging the gap of time before the stirring of new attitudes of mind would bring their strange science into the world of open discussion again.

The mid-nineteenth century saw the origin of many unexpected religious and occult movements. The stresses of the new society were bound to result in this kind of release activity. Mankind was impelled to seek out some reason in life; the apparent injustices and the abandonment of old attitudes towards religion made this search imperative. Yet the cleansing of old beliefs was a difficult and slow process. The religious bodies adopted new charitable attitudes towards their members. It must be remembered, however, that the encyclical *Rerum Novarum*, which spoke of social justice in a Christian Europe, came long after the bitter social struggles which led to the Communist Manifesto and the short-lived Paris Commune. It is not surprising that the strictly materialist approach to human problems rapidly became dominant. Religious revival and the dramatic assault on social evils mounted by the Salvation Army were important manifestations affecting the masses. The spread of universal education opened many more minds to the possibilities of life and the position of man as an intellectual being. The comfortable middle classes turned towards more interesting experiments. We find a renewed interest in esoteric religion, the influence of Eastern beliefs through the new Theosophists, the development of ancient experience in a formal way through the re-created Spiritualists, and the influence of direct visionary experiences which created new types of faith such as Mormonism. These were all part of the human quest for enlightenment at a time when the growth of a universal mechanistic civilization posed the eternal question of the destiny of mankind.

Alchemy could not play an important part in the dark chaos which accompanied the birth of new concepts of civilization. It had been a system of philosophy and a way of life only to the select few. The alchemist had been the learned scholar primarily, and the illuminated outsider only very rarely. Alchemical disciplines were not for the mass of the people. The literature on the subject was purposely confused, contradictory and obscurantist. Ideas from alchemical thought were quite openly expressed in many religious groups; but it could not really be acknowledged that they were following an ancient cult which had been thoroughly disproven by chemists and physicists. It would seem as sensible as acting out a fairy tale. There had even been a fragmentation of the philosophic ideas expressed by the old alchemists. It seems that some people in remote regions managed to carry on a kind of experimental side of the cult; but they were known only to fellow occultists. The way of the old-time alchemist survived mainly in Islamic communities. It was semi-secret, old-fashioned, and patient. The philosophic doctrines were so abstruse that they appealed only to the few, but they were alive and respected. Only in the European world could they be without effect, because of the European view that civilization was expressed only by mechanical and technological advancement. In parts of Europe the tradition may have been carried on, in fact it is said to have survived largely among Jewish scholars interested in the study of the *Kabbalah*. This may be true, but kabbalistic studies are not necessarily alchemy. They are part of the basic study of the nature of God's relationship with His creation, and so must have many points of intellectual contact with alchemy.

The best work on alchemy in the dark periods of the nineteenth century, *A Suggestive Enquiry into the Hermetic Mystery*, was published in London in 1850, although the authoress, Mary Anne Atwood (née South) withdrew as many copies as she could buy back or beg from her friends as possible. The reason was certainly not a reflection of the public scepticism about alchemy, but was based on her fears that she had stumbled on a great secret and had thoughtlessly revealed too much. She refused to speak more on the subject of her studies, even though she lived until 1910 when she died at the age of ninety-seven. She expressed the view that the secret of the alchemists was the perfection of the soul; and that those who would follow the secret path should seek a great part of their own way. If they were led too easily into these studies they might indeed find themselves on the brink of disaster. She was emphatic about the old rule that the worker was one with the work. A wrong state of mind in the worker could cause untold harm.

Today we have seen how the development of a new and wonderful power – atomic energy – has been bedevilled by the political and military minds which have directed it towards the threat of ultimate destruction.

Mrs Atwood was a bridge between the older alchemists and the modern students of their works. As far as we know her interests were purely literary and historical and she performed no alchemical experiments. Her father, Mr Thomas South of Gosport, was a philosophically minded man who was interested in the study of religion, including the classical philosophers. He collected a large library of rare books on his favourite subjects and added to it as his investigations spread towards the history of the Hermetic tradition. He saw quite clearly that there was a direct thread of tradition from the secret knowledge of the ancient Mysteries through to the secret tradition of the alchemists. From childhood his daughter followed his studies, and became proficient in Greek and Latin; she was able to help with the index he needed to classify the ancient knowledge. In this way, by indexing and reading, she began to understand that within all the mystification of the ancient and medieval writers there was a thread of understanding of an ancient truth about the relationship of the soul to the divine powers, the possibility of attaining a process of spiritual enlightenment.

Apparently at some period of her studies in the then modern phenomena of spiritualism and hypnosis she suddenly became aware that those rather boring exercises which appeared to lead to nowhere, had a close link with the past. She published a pamphlet entitled *Early Magnetism in its Higher Relations to Humanity as veiled in the Poets and the Prophets*. It was published anonymously, but created a stir in the circles which were still interested in the study of ecstatic beliefs. The little essay seems to have been the result of some kind of sudden realization of the link between past and present, accompanied by a vision of light; the kind of experience which the mystics call illumination.

In a few years Miss South had taken her studies to a point where at the age of thirty-seven she had completed her major work, *A Suggestive Enquiry into the Hermetic Mystery*. After about a hundred copies had been sold a sudden panic fell upon both Mr South and his daughter. A long manuscript poem about alchemy, which Mr South had written, and every copy of the book which could be bought-in were immolated on a sacrificial pyre on the lawn of the house at Gosport. After that still further efforts were made to gather in other copies of the work but enough survived to enable the Julian Press of New York to issue a reprint in 1960.

After the burning of books neither of the writers made any large contribution to alchemical literature. They had no wish to open the mysteries. There can be little doubt that at that period they were right. As the lady wrote later, when she was happily married to the Rev. A. T. Atwood, the profusion of charlatans and false teachers made it imperative that the book should be destroyed to save its teaching from falling into the wrong hands. She and her father had been impressed by their discoveries. That is practically all we know.

The book itself was a systematized collection of material from many sources of many periods. Its novelty was in the arrangement of material. There are translations of old texts; Miss South composed a general critical framework to unite them, and attempted to form the work into a connected whole. In later life she thought the book ill constructed and hardly worthy of the attempt to realize the great truths of the ancient alchemical philosophy. She was quite right; yet the book is a very good guide to the unity of thought which ran through the ancient and medieval teachings on the subject. In many ways she anticipated the psychological studies made by C. G. Jung. She realized that the real aim of the alchemists was to induce a state of enlightenment in which they became at one with the universe and could be reached directly by God. She also understood what the adepts meant in their many warnings that the path of enlightenment was inward.

No doubt Mrs Atwood's early contacts with the Spiritualist circles and the study of Mesmerism made her much more sensitive to the non-material side of the alchemical philosophy. She was acquainted with many of the phenomena of the séance room, and knew of the strange states of trance and hypnotism which were mentioned often enough under the accounts of divine inspiration, or demonic possession in ancient times. The links with the ancient world were clear to her, but of course few of her contemporaries

## The Seventeenth Century: Drawings

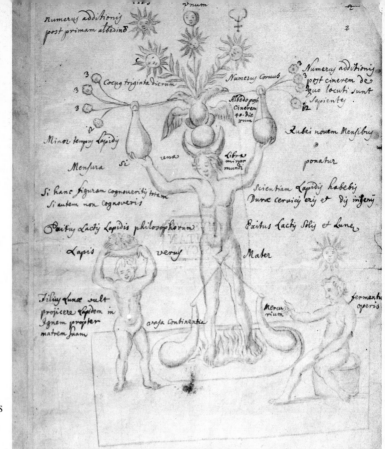

Beginning of the process
for preparing the Stone.
The moon receives the
planetary powers

The burning of the
earth-animal and the
extraction of the white
and red elixirs

Ex stellis generantur Pluviæ

Mortuus est draco cum
fratre et matre sua

Accipe spiritu nouum

& surge quid dormis

Memento homo quia
& noster

cinis es & in cinerem reuerteris

Sitio et mortuus
sum

Si sitis da ei potum
& viuet

Surrexit post nouem lonam

Hermes pater
phylosophorum

Mensura potati
onis Aqua perma
nens est
et aqua
vitæ

Qui lotus est nd
indiget nisi ut pedes
lauet ut sit mun
= dus totus.

Amplius nd uolatis mecum

Lucerna pedibus meis est lumen ocu=
lorum meorum. Ignorabo principio
reliqua Ignorantur.

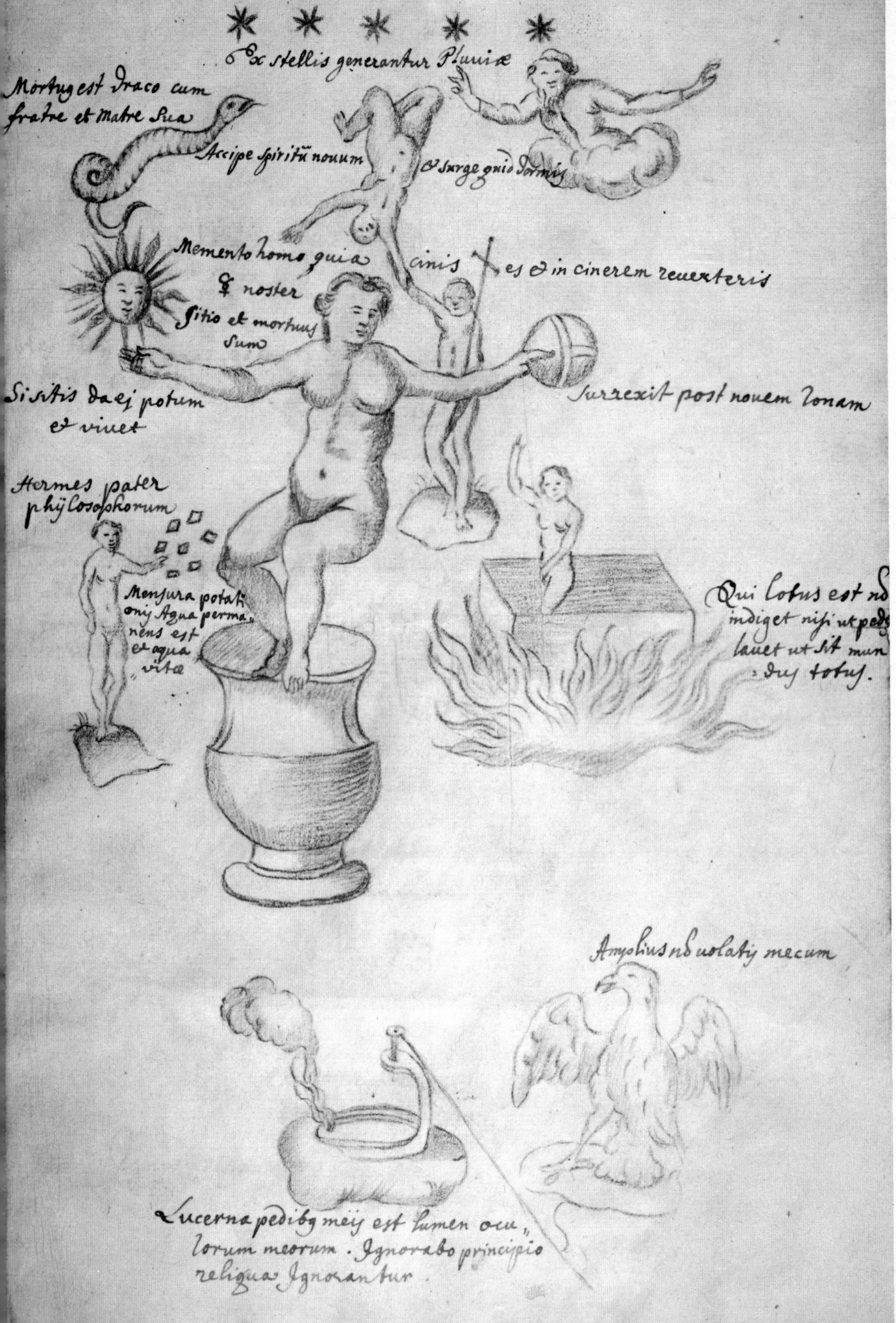

The crowned
Alchymia passing her
waters like Noah's
flood on the highest
mountains

*Opposite:* Symbols of
the eternal between
death and resurrection
shown in the Process

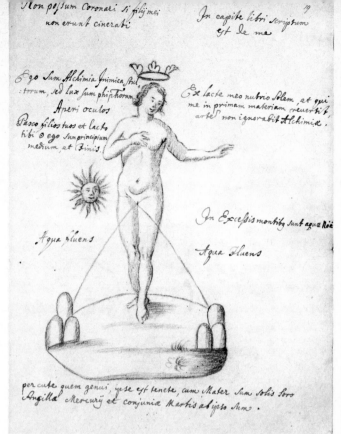

The use of the furnace to produce
the philosophic essences

The virgin between Sun and Moon,
who is inspired by the bird of
Sun, Moon and Azoth

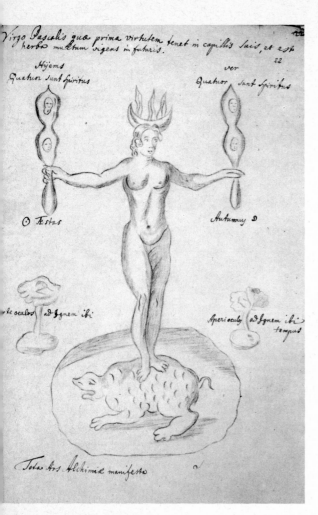

The Paschal Virgin between Moon and Earth as the symbol of the totality of alchemical art

The beginning of the Stone where the dragon and the phoenix combine as a reflux furnace

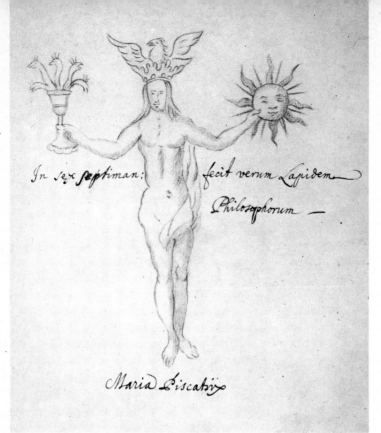

*In sex septiman: fecit verum Lapidem Philosophorum —*

*Maria Piscatrix*

*Maria Piscatrix*; the philosopher's stone crowned with the phoenix and holding the grail and the Sun

The light of the philosophers: the elixirs, shown as red and white roses, for the transmutation to silver

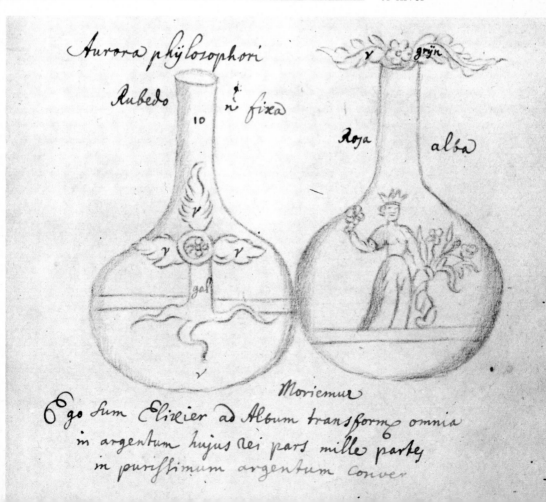

*Aurora phÿlosophori*

*Rubedo ☿ ñ fixa*

10

*Roſa alba*

*grÿn*

*Moriemur*

*Ego ſum Elixier ad Album transform omnia in argentum hujus rei pars mille partes in puriſſimum argentum Conver*

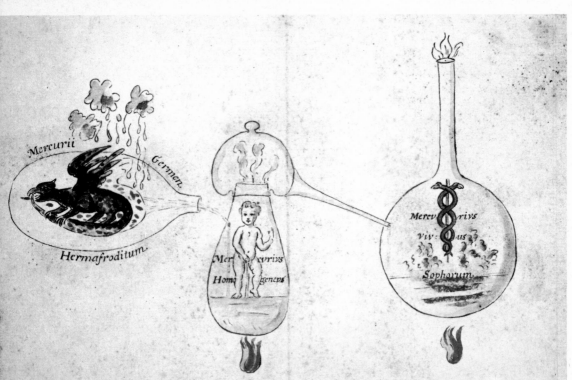

Pages from the *Cabala Mineralis Rabbi Simeon ben Cantara*
*Above:* The source of the alchemist's materials
*Below:* The purification of the philosophic mercury

The calcination of
Luna and Sol

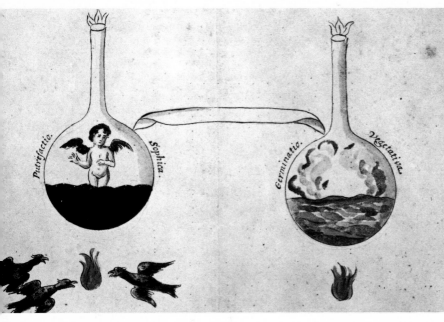

Putrefaction is
followed by
germination

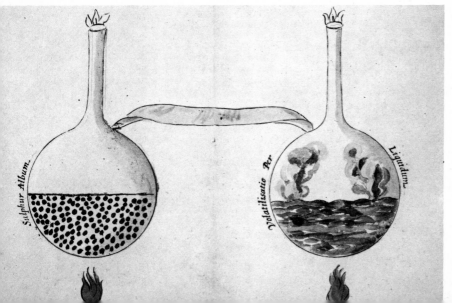

The White Sulphur
is volatilized to
display the peacock's
tail

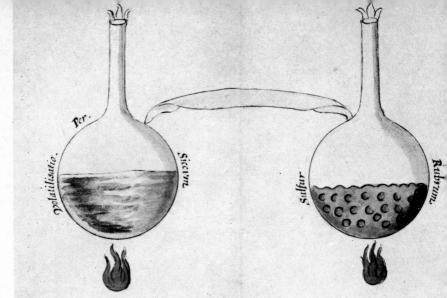

Volatilization to procure the Red Sulphur

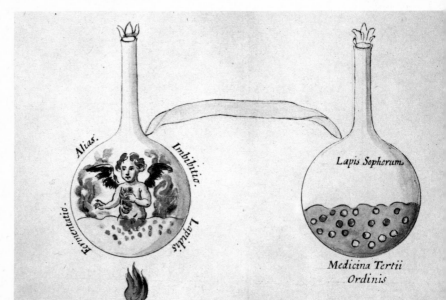

Mercury added to Red Sulphur putrefies and then germinates the elixir of projection

Blessed be the Creator and His works

had the advantage of her extensive acquaintance with the literature of the subject. But she also saw something very clearly that made her feel it would be dangerous to give the power into the hands of an evil-intentioned student. Was this simply the knowledge of Mesmerism? Or was it some special discovery about the nature of the human mind and the way in which the deep unconscious can tap apparently impossible sources of information? Or did she step through time and see something of the horror of realized transmutation used for destruction? We shall probably never know this. But the book which was left by Mrs Atwood has great value as a work of philosophical alchemy which embodies many useful quotations from her father's fine library of specialist works.

Further advances in the study were inhibited in Europe and America as Mrs Atwood had seen only too well. The sincere students of Spiritualism were hampered by the activities of hordes of charlatans. The whole world in that period was much inhibited by a tendency to follow materialist doctrines. The scientists were as narrowly constrained by the supposed immutability of their rules as any monastic body. Later they came to realize that within the immutable rules there were other rules obtaining for other conditions. It took a great deal of struggle and pain for the civilized world to break a way through the dark tunnel of the nineteenth century. In the sphere of morals there was a curious attempt to adapt a puritanical social system to the instinctive life, which resulted in the 'double-standard' theories. It would not work, but nobody realized just what was happening until Sigmund Freud began to find a pattern in the nervous breakdowns which were occurring all round him, even in cultured and gay Vienna. Were the religious cranks, and founders of the new sects all victims of the curious sub-conscious aspects of the mind? People had waking dreams, were deluded in daylight, and behaved in a peculiar manner because of the eruption of material which was at first thought to have come from a kind of dustbin into which the conscious personality had dumped displeasing or immoral ideas.

It could easily be said now that the ancient peoples had all kinds of psychic experiences which revealed their own neuroses. In fact Freud, working on very sound grounds of really parallel situations, names some of the complexes which he discovered in the heroes of the classical legends whose behaviour had exhibited similar characteristics. A complex was a little group of related ideas which seemed to escape from the totality of the intellect and work almost as if it had become an independent personality inhabiting the body of the patient. So here was the explanation of demonic possession! Maybe the delusions of so many alchemists about gold were also expositions of a curiously linked group of ideas which, because of the methods of their art, had become isolated together with their imagery as a huge delusional complex.

New ideas and new ways of thought were beginning. A new attitude towards the curious accounts of the alchemical experience had become possible. Perhaps an alchemist was in danger of being invited to relax on a hard couch and tell his ideas about word association, but at least this would be better than being thought a necromancer, or a cheat. In any case the public attitude towards the odd individual was becoming more sympathetic. The psychoanalysts had cured many people of their terrible inhibitions and the sexual tensions which arose from the long constraint of civilized man in a dark tunnel of inhibition.

The new attitude of science towards the alchemists was that they were respected ancestors who had wandered into a wilderness of false hypotheses. Little notice was taken of the spiritual side of alchemy by the scientists, nor was the making of alchemical gold and the meaning of the material elixirs of transmutation taken into consideration by the psychologists. Again there was a pair of opposites which needed reconciliation. Though this process of reconciliation is by no means complete it has achieved some interesting new dimensions through the work of Freud's one-time associate, C. G. Jung. The division was largely over whether the secret inner mind was a sub-conscious dustbin, or really the basic part of the whole personality of the individual. Were dreams disguises for pornography we dare not face in ourselves, or were they often indications of our progress through a life process having striking parallels with alchemy?

# 11

# the inner space

That alchemy stems from a religious discipline is certain. Its philosophy led the experimenters towards a way of life in which a due modesty of demeanour was demanded. Wealth might come, but ambition for wealth was a deterrent to progress. The granting of enlightenment came from above. In the practical aspects of the work chemical reactions were observed, and they had a curious effect on the observer. The dragons and lions, the royal pair and the planetary metals all come within the literature, yet they could not have been observed in those forms within the alembics and crucibles of the workshop. They were more than image associations, more of the nature of 'pictures in the fire'. In fact they became part of the private mythology of the alchemists. Individuals differed in the sequence of events and the pattern of the figures to some extent, but there was a basic series of appearances which all came in sequence and were expressed in descriptive terms which had practically no relationship with the real facts of observation.

In the twentieth century it became possible to study these confused ideas and find a pattern in them. It was a special contribution by C. G. Jung, that he found that they were reflected in the dreams and daydreams of some of his most intelligent patients. They represented a kind of mythology which developed from qualities inherent in the human personality.

The discoveries of Jung do not describe the material side of alchemy, nor do they explain the very few cases in which real material results were achieved under circumstances which are clear. Nevertheless this also fits into the pattern of synchronisms which Jung studied as a fact without rational explanation.

However, the path of the alchemist was clearly the path of an intelligent human being moving through many crises towards the discovery of his own soul. That was said by most of the famous alchemists to be the real purpose of the work; and there can be no doubt that such a perfection of the soul was the purpose of the ancient mystery religions from which the first alchemists elaborated their doctrines.

Although the alchemists were always limited in numbers, and usually did not care to congregate, they held their opinions very staunchly. The almost identical attitudes among the more important individuals among them shows that the pattern of their mystical art was very powerful. It was conditioned by tradition, but only changed in its outward form. The outward forms evolved through the development of technical apparatus. The old *kerotakis* became the still and alembic. The small charcoal fire became a system of properly constructed furnaces. Yet the inner tradition of the meanings of the alchemical process became elaborated only towards the end. Perhaps the original teaching was elaborate enough to satisfy most teachers.

The system was so emotionally powerful that although many alchemists were ruined in the search for their goal they counted it worth while. Only those looking for the gold of this world cursed their fate and abandoned the research. The alchemists regarded the search for material wealth as a trap, and they were the more happy if the mysterious powers beyond them gave the power of transmutation. The search was all-absorbing, and the mystery so great that they could not explain it to their fellows. In fact they were well aware that the inner knowledge they sought must not be divulged indiscriminately. It was a secret as powerful as the holy Kabbalah itself, for it was the secret of how the universe was created, of how the centre and the circumference were one, how all things were related in an inner unity of material.

It is probable that the experience of the Greco-Egyptian ritual around the process displayed in the *kerotakis* drew the devotees to concentrate their visionary world on the alchemical process. The archetypes seen as projections in the process display quite a different form from that seen in the ecstatic rituals of Dionysian cults. The aim of peace of soul and enlightenment was the same. It is still the same in some modern psychedelic study groups. The high point is the inner illumination, even if it is estimated intellectually and not as a deep experience of the inner and greater personality.

The success of the old alchemists cannot be measured by any standards of today. They appear to have achieved a peace of soul, and a certain modesty of personal appearance which made them inconspicuous. It was the false or the perverted alchemist who became the subject of the poets and playwrights.

The illustrations will show the nature of the myths which they built up from the archetypal material released during their experimental studies. One of the great early adventures was discovering the moon who was to pair with their sun. She was the feminine half of the work, and was refined silver, and yet behaved as a necessary opposite to the active power of sol. If the process was really an inward journey she was the equivalent of *anima* for the male alchemist.

At first she is a terrifying creature, since she often appears as a Melusina. Part animal part woman she has great charm, but often becomes somewhat terrifying by the savage way in which she shows her vulva, not as a haven of delight, but as a place of terror and destruction. She would not have had that aspect if the alchemists had had any idea of the true place of women in their universe. But of course she is an early stage of the manifestation of the opposite in nature. She appears in legends all over the world. She is actually a figure of the earth, which both devours the dead and gives life to the newly born. A dark power of life, she is seen by primitive people as a terrible goddess, and by the wiser peoples of antiquity as the primitive mother of being.

This natural and yet frightening earth has to be placed in the vessel, and put on the waters to be purified by fire. Then the sun appears and the moon, glowing in the waters of creation (or the vapours from the heating process). The new powers are like children. They have life and creative power coming from the suffering of their mother who has been freed by the dragon. They are distilled and redistilled. The adept realizes that they must be destroyed, as his own youthful fantasies have to be destroyed. He then sees that the breaking up and roasting results in a fine white powder. All is changed by a total destruction of life which will yet flower again. The glowing ash still has its human form. The ash is then placed on a ship to sail the dark seas to an unknown destination. Mercury is the guide. The ashes again assume bodily form, but the new man is in a higher state, refined or distilled, from the putrefactions of earth. In this long voyage in the vessel over the dark waters (the purified *materia prima* is passing through sessions of slow heating in a vessel, sometimes being treated by acids such as the Green Dragon, or hydrochloric acid, sometimes being cleansed by herbal drenches of distillates like alcohol) the planets surround the sufferer, and each one being also a metal beams influences which balance up to a new life, compounded of all life. This is likened to the emergence from the fire, as the turning into the new phoenix born from the egg laid as the old phoenix bursts into flames.

Then the new Mercury and the new Venus must mate. The sun and the moon must perfect the life of the cosmos in intimate union, both purified and crowned with the purest gold. The son of the union is a wonderful form of the androgynous Mercurius; he is the bearer of life and change, for he is also the guide of souls. Yet as this wondrous child appears he must be seized upon by time. For time is the parent of this world, the movements of the planetary children are dictated by time. In the event the father, Chronos, devours his planetary children. This is the end of the Paradise Garden. Often the garden appears in the later manuscripts with the four-square lawn hedged by high growing bushes, and in the centre a four-square pond in which the figures in the vision bathe naked at the foot of the tree of life. Yet this tree has come from earlier stages since it contains a Melusina figure and springs from the head of the woman and the penis of the man. It is the Tree of Life, an analogue of Yggdrasil which spans the gulf from Nifelheim to the bright world of Valhalla.

It is a problem to move into another state, for this beautiful dreamland is not the answer to the mysteries, it is simply the beauty of the universe in its ineffable orderliness. So mankind has to go on the journey to timelessness or completion, and it is when the child is swallowed by Chronos that the further path to unity opens. The journey is difficult. It is usually seen as a journey through complex passages before emerging into another place and finding the way is still not complete. One cannot go on without aid, and it is then that the soul who truly understands that the *materia prima*, the matter of the universe, is somehow within him is faced by illumination. It is a light without flame, it is the burning bush which is not consumed, it is the heart of the rose.

Whatever illumination may be it leaves a permanent mark on the character. Our alchemist is sure that he has reached the ultimate stage and has been through so many purifications that he is made into the gold which is not common gold. After this his strange gentleness of character earns him a kind of oblivion. Tranquillity and equilibrium of mind are his marks. He is unostentatious and goes about his business. The association with the ability to perform the material act of transmutation seems to come when the enlightenment has been achieved fairly early in life, in middle age.

It is just at this point that we meet the central problem of alchemy. The art was a passage through dramatic experiences while experimenting with material things. The pains taken and the costs accepted for the work to be accomplished became very great. This does not seem to have been essential, for the early Alexandrian apparatus and materials were not of great value in worldly terms, and in the last days of alchemy it is stated that the Stone was something of little value and the process was not long in a real sense, though tradition made it appear to cover years. Nevertheless, all this work was performed with a real laboratory. The urge to continue experimenting was overwhelming, and real ruin as well as possible disgrace were faced by the few for the sake of the hidden knowledge. In some cases there was evidence of a curious power to make base metals turn into gold by apparently simple means. This we cannot explain. The experiments can be repeated with little result. The meaning of the curious visionary creatures which were used as descriptions of chemical substances has been made clear by modern chemists. Yet at some point in this process the alchemist acquires a super-human modesty and a power which may bring him unexpectedly to help a friendly soul make a transmutation of mercury or lead to gold. This, according to present knowledge, is quite insane. It cannot be done. The alchemists answer simply that it was done. It was done by men to whom it was no longer important.

The few examples which seem reasonable were apparently intended as a demonstration of the possibility of transmutation. There was no very good reason for the experience of Helvetius, except that he was in a position to testify to good effect. The amount of gold was not important, the financial position of Helvetius was sound, and the people of the Netherlands at that period were rich and flourishing. Here was no charity such as was dis-pensed by the wise Nicolas Flamel and Pernelle, but an exposition which apparently leads nowhere. Was it a last sign before the power left the heart of mankind? Or was it simply an affirmation of a will to remain until time had brought about a new understanding? Each person must draw his own conclusions.

What was the reason, or sense, of following up alchemy at all? We have no modern experience to tell us, at least in the field of public knowledge. The old art did lead to a great blessing in the achievement of psychological integration, but was it worth the sacrifices made by the adepts?

If there is an explanation of the alchemical gold it is in the field of the nature of the integrated personality. The conscious mind in the integrated person is known to be but a small part of the wonderful whole which embraces a vast unconscious realm, partly personal but also including a measureless region where the individual is in touch with the whole of material creation. It is as if a person were able to visualize developed humanity as a series of mountain peaks, rising from the immensity of the whole of the material universe. This knowledge cannot be known; it is an experience of wholeness-with-everything-which-is; so was Illumination, for the adept became aware of nature as a whole.

The final step to be taken in the spiritual progress of the adept was im-possible for him to make alone. His studies had led him to a knowledge of the works of God, and he realized that through all the complexities of nature there ran an essential unity. This he visualized as an imponderable fluid from which all things took their form and which was the basis from which various degrees of impurity formed the differing earths and metals. It is not unlike our view of electricity, but seen in a poetic rather than a scientific way. But to the adept all this universe was the work of a conscious creator. He was not to identify himself with anything but the material universe. The creator was both within everything and transcending everything, for the creator could not be simply confined within the created. Having purified his heart by the prayers and code of self discipline current in his period the adept waited for the coming of the light.

The expected light was something utterly beyond the imagination. It was something in which the adept was engulfed and altered. The experience was not to be described in terms which we can fully understand. We hear of the terror as well as the beauty, and note that the adept was often a changed personality after the experience. The ecstatic experience was the crown of the alchemist's life, but it was not always comforting. We have two Christian parallels, in St Paul who was waylaid and shattered with the Light on the Damascus road, and ever afterwards went on his way towards martyrdom; and in St Francis of Assisi who suffered the vision which implanted most painful stigmata to add to his virtues and complete absorption as well as his physical breakdown. The alchemists expected little more. Their path, however, had been through the mystical sciences and so some of them appear to have been given the gift of transmutation, or so they claimed, all with a humility which is very much in their favour.

One could hardly canonize an alchemist as such, because he was concerned with the making of gold. Those of the Doctors of the Church who were interested in alchemy were canonized for their other activities as teachers and organizers. Their sanctity was shown in the performance of the impossible by miracles of healing and helping and not for the feats of transmutation. So in the medieval era the good alchemist was really the learned man who was also a holy man. In the Christian world he was often an Abbot or Canon. In the Islamic world he ranked with the great teachers. The alchemist was silent about the mystery of the art, but he was usually neither poor nor obscure.

In post-Reformation times in Europe the alchemist became much more the philosopher, and was usually so concerned with the relationship between the created and the creator that he became more and more a Christian mystic. But he also became something else . . . a member of an unorganized community of adepts. These people were linked with the developments of the Rosicrucian mysteries, and with some of the developments of later

# Lambspringk

Frontispiece: the
philosopher
Lambspringk with
his furnace

First figure: spirit
and soul swim like
fishes in the body of
the water

Second figure: Mars and the dragon—a death-struggle symbolizing putrefaction

Third figure: stag and unicorn in the forest; soul and spirit are embodied

Fourth figure: lion and lioness, spirit and soul are united in the body

Fifth figure: dog and wolf struggle but will be united as one

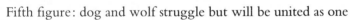

Sixth figure: within the dragon is its own healing. Mercury is liquid but can become coagulated

Seventh figure: two birds in the forest will become one. Mercury must be sublimed and then coagulated to slow its movement

Eighth figure: two birds fight and one devours the other. Slowly heat the material so that the body becomes white and the spirit red

Ninth figure: the Lord of the Forests has risen from the lowest to the highest position. The tincture has reached its first degree

Tenth figure: the tincture must be treated by fire in order to augment its power

Eleventh figure: body, soul and spirit are reunited as Father, Son and Guide

Twelfth figure: the spirit and soul have climbed the Mountain of India which lies within the alchemical vessel

Thirteenth figure: the father must devour the son in order that soul and spirit may be freed from the body

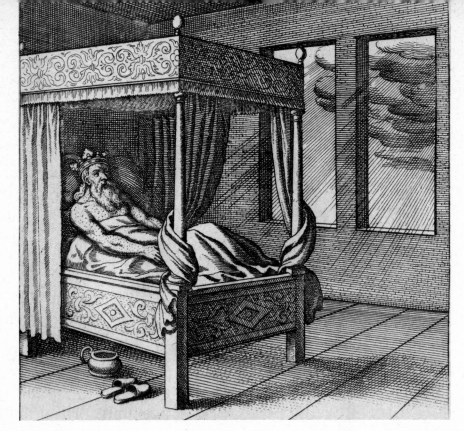

Fourteenth figure: the fevered father sweats the tincture of the wise from his body

Fifteenth figure: here father and son are joined in unity by the spirit; and so they will remain for ever more

Masonic cults. The adept in this world was always mysterious. We hear of his appearances, and of the strange wealth surrounding him, though he remained very modest in personal life. He was usually accompanied by his wife, but involved in deepest secrecy.

The modern alchemist is also a retiring personality. A few are to be found publishing notes of experiments. A few have left stories that link their thought with a deep philosophy of the nature of the universe and of man. There are whispered claims that the secret has been found. However, it is best to treat the modern survival of the alchemical tradition as a matter of uncertainty. The student in the old times was approached by the adepts. Perhaps it remains still the same today.

We have now looked at the historical story of the alchemists. There has not been room to discuss all of them, for in their periods of success and brilliance there were many who wrote disguised accounts of their work. Charlatans were many, but mostly they can be separated from the retiring and modest adepts. Yet the mysteries of the beginning and end of this spagiric art remain.

There were probably many beginnings, because so many of the traditions of the early writers stem from the mystery religions of antiquity. There are traces of Orphic thought from Greece, of Zoroastrian and Manichaean ideas from Persia, of rituals of the gods of Babylon and Assyria and of the fertility rituals of Egypt. All through alchemical history the ideas of the parallels with fertility and sexuality remain marked. Just as it was holy in the ancient world, and seen as an activity shared by gods and men, sex became something special to the Christian alchemists, who saw it as the transmission of life which came originally from the uncreated to be given to man and all other living forms of nature. The mystery was expressed in the writings and symbols of alchemy. Probably from time to time it had its active expression in reality, especially in the fourteenth to sixteenth centuries. But basically the alchemist was seeking the ideas of unity and conjunction of opposites through their manifestation in inanimate nature. His chemical works were attempts to produce this coalescence and generation in a series of events which produced the pure perfected metal, philosophic gold, from the apparent rubbish of the *materia prima*.

One may note that to the Egyptians the fertile Nile mud was the analogue of the Marsh of Creation in which Hathor moves; but the period of sexual repression in the early Middle Ages brought forth an idea that the material to be used was human ordure. We find many recipes for brewing up faeces and urine, which give a distinctly Freudian picture of repressions in the cloistered life.

153

The endings of alchemy have not been reached, neither in the development of the personal psyche, nor in the making of the medicines which give perfect health and the perfect gold. The retreat of the alchemist into the position of the hidden philosopher is quite proper psychologically. He is taking the position of the wise old man who appears in dreams to open the way to the treasure house of the unconscious.

The eruption of the intellect was the beginning of true chemistry, and the obscurance of the alchemical philosophy. As this portion of our personality became more conscious it produced wonderful advances in the life of mankind. It was absolutely necessary for the advance of science that the old alchemical methods, full of dream contents and obscurantism, should pass away. It was also necessary that the more self-conscious life achieved by mankind should have an inner alchemy which would lead to the unconscious contents of the personality reaching up towards an integration. This was the goal of the mystery religions and of the alchemists. This process is still largely without achievement. Mankind knows the mathematics of the universe and has not found a way to reconcile the opposites. The spagiric art, the art of union between circumference and centre, has not been achieved. Opposites are created and not resolved but threatened by violent repressions. The secret of the mathematical universe has produced the power of destruction. Opposites, instead of uniting, threaten to achieve mutual annihilation.

There is still some room for the study of alchemy as a philosophy even under the new circumstances of the present age.

The unconscious mind is stirring and attempts to bring its powers into consciousness are more successful in the psychiatric consulting room. A new kind of alchemy of colour and sensation to produce illumination is to be found in the present movement of psychedelic art. Something like it was once tried by the ancient Sufi mystics and the early Isma'ili sects, but with new sound and colour the mind is quietened and the cerebral cortex stimulated to give a modern version of illumination. Whether this will prove to be merely a recrudescence of the old mysteries like the Dionysian cults is uncertain. So far it has found no wise alchemist to plan the periods and processes, so that in the end, spiritual gold is forthcoming.

However, mankind today has new knowledge both of the material structure of the universe and of the organic nature of the human psyche. There is yet hope of the union of opposites and the birth of a golden age.

# 12

# the words of power

In the foregoing pages of history we have not discussed the strange literature which has grown around the subject of alchemy. We have only so far mentioned the *Tabula Smaragdina*; although it is the mystic root of almost all subsequent statements, it is basically a document of outstanding clarity. Its mystery is simply that the philosophic statement is not made clear.

In all other alchemical works the principle is the same. Much is written down, and usually with some accuracy, but the links which would open the alchemical path to all enquirers are missing. Sometimes the writer will lead one into deep religious speculation, sometimes he will open a beautiful garden of verbal flowers; but always he has the fear that the unworthy will find the power and make evil use of it. Because of that fear alchemists have deliberately chosen to die rather than reveal their secrets.

All throughout the book, and in all the greater works on alchemy, there is a feeling of a double path. There is the class of opposites, of aboveness with belowness, of air with earth, of fire with water. To the alchemist the double path was really one. It was the road to perfection. Alchemists understood that one reached perfection only through the power given from above to those who abandoned their lower nature to make the ascent. It was a road which led the soul to enlightenment and the knowledge of the spirit of a living Universe. Jung would have called it a process of individuation. The psychological benefits were exactly of that type. The more recent alchemists understood it to be what was taught in the mysteries of Eleusis and elsewhere, in ancient times. But they also expected that the truly enlightened alchemist who had rejected the desire for personal riches or power would be blessed by the attainment of the philosopher's stone which would make gold, materially. For the alchemist, the double path was so much a part of nature, that, in purifying himself through the discipline of long years in study and laboratory experience, he could also purify the natural materials he used, so that they became true and perfect gold.

The essential attitude has probably never been better put than in a short passage from the ancient book attributed to Hermes Trismegistus, *The Divine Poimandres* (or *Shepherd*).

Whatever is concerned with physical operations and work on matter has a bodily form. These operations and workings are not carried upward but by their nature they tend downward (to union with matter). Earthly things cannot do good to those in Heaven, but all heavenly things bring aid to things on earth. Heaven is the place of eternal bodies. Earth is the receptacle of the corruptible bodies. Earth is without reason; Heaven is truly rational The things of Heaven are beneath it. The things of earth are above it. Heaven is the first created Element. Earth is the last of elements.

In a text so early that its true origin has always been disputed, Hermes sets forth the goal of the alchemist: the state by which union can be reached between heaven and earth, through the intervention of higher powers. It is a logical step from the primitive belief that the separated powers of earth and sky should be reunited by magical chants and ritual. The picture derived from the world of nature has now a richer connotation.

The theme of inspiration is constant in alchemical literature. Here is a portion of the *Golden Tractate of Hermes Trismegistus*, which may go back to the fourth or fifth century with earlier fragments and later additions. Like all the great alchemical works it is of mixed origin.

Even thus said Hermes: I have not ceased to experiment through long years, neither have I spared myself from mental toil. Yet have I attained this science, this Art, alone from the inspiration of the Living God, who thought fit to open the mystery to me, His servant. To those who are enabled to understand Truth through their reason He has given power to make choice but to none will he permit the opportunity for evil.

... Now you shall understand that the Ancient Philosophers made division of the Water to separate it into four substances; one to two and three to one; the one third part of which is colour; which is a coagulating moisture; but the other two thirds are the Weights of the Wise.

Take an ounce and a half of the humidity; and of the Midday Redness, the soul of gold, take a fourth part which is half an ounce. Of the citrine Seyre take similarly half an ounce. Of the Auripigment take half (which are eight) thus making a total of three ounces; and you must know that the Vine of the Wise is drawn forth in three, and the Wine of it is perfected in Thirty.

Therefore understand the work: decoction lessens the matter, but the tincture augments it, because the Moon (Luna) is diminished after fifteen days and in the third she increases. This is the beginning and the end.

Now I have declared that which has been concealed, since the work is both with you and around you. Taking the inner fixed substance you may find it either in Earth or Sea.

There is much more in the *Golden Tractate*, for its language is capable of explanation. Unfortunately for us it is rather like an equation with many answers. None of the named substances are what they seem. The *Golden Tractate* continues through its complex webs of symbolic utterances and attains a climax which again contains evidence of antiquity, and of medieval translation from an Arabic version. The curious search for a substance called 'ixir', comes from a translation of 'elixir' of which the first syllable is taken to be the Arabic definite article equivalent to our 'the'.

O sons of Wisdom know that there are Seven bodies of which Gold is the first, it is the head, the most perfect, the king of them all. Earth cannot corrupt it, nor fire ruin it, nor can the water change it. Its appearance is even and its nature is regulated in respect of the action of heat, cold and moisture. There is nothing in it which is superfluous to it. Therefore the Philosophers have honoured and praised it comparing it with the sun among the stars and stating that all matter is made more perfect by its light. As every vegetable creature and all fruits of earth are by the will of God perfected by the Sun; so Gold which is the ferment Ixir inspirits and also contains every metallic body.

Just as dough cannot be made to rise without a ferment, so the material must be sublimed and purified. The uncleanness must be separated from the excrement, and then one must mix them again in conjunction, and add the ferment which will confect the earth with water until the Ixir will ferment just as the bakers' dough ferments. Consider this carefully, meditate on it. Note that the ferment changes the natures of the former substances to another thing. Note also that there is no ferment to be obtained except from something of a kindred nature.

You will see that the ferment whitens the mixture and while preventing combustion it holds the tincture and stops it from flying away. It rejoices the bodies and makes them to enter into one another and join intimately. This is the Key of the Philosophers and the end of their works. Through this Science bodies are adjusted and through the assistance of God their working is consummated.

Remember that negligence in the operation and false ideas of the matter of it will pervert the whole work. This is like using bad leaven on the dough, or making curds for cheese, or putting musk among the aromatic odours.

The colour of the golden matter points to redness, and its nature is not sweetness. Therefore we must make Seriacum from them, which is to say Ixir. And we make encaustic from them as we have written. With the King's Seal we have tinted the clay and thereby have set forth the colour of Heaven, which strengthens the sight of all who see it.

The Stone, therefore, is most precious spotless Gold. It is evenly tempered so that neither fire, air, water nor earth have power to corrupt it. This is the

Universal Ferment which will purify all things by its composition of the true citrine or yellow colour.

The Gold of the Wise, concocted and well digested with fiery water, makes Ixir. The Gold of the Wise is heavier than lead, which in a moderate mixture is the ferment Ixir, but on the contrary it becomes disorganized by an equal composition.

The Work begins from the Vegetable, next from the Animal as in the egg of the hen in which is the great support. Our earth is gold, of all of which we make Seriacum, which is the ferment Ixir.

So much for the *Golden Tractate*. It is both wise and foolish, confused and clear. This is typical of alchemy during any period of history.

Another famous alchemical work comes from Renaissance times. It is a supposed inscription on a marble tomb slab from Bologna. True it may have been composed by some young philosophic doctor from Bologna, the oldest and most respected university in Europe; yet whoever made the poem was aware of the Etruscan linkages with Bologna. The use of the full triple name of a woman is Etruscan rather than Latin, and indeed the clan name of the lady, Laelia, is a reference to a powerful Etruscan gens which lasted throughout their history. It may be that there is a tradition here from an earlier period than the Renaissance. The alchemists were impressed by the poem and devoted many pages to its interpretation. Maybe the best explanation is that the male and female personages who are commemorated (yet whose attributes add up to nothing at all) are simply the hidden life forces in nature, which are indeed the forces which the alchemists hoped would be given into their hands if they were found worthy of the trust. Here is the poem:

> AELIA LAELIA CRISPIS,
> Not a man, nor a woman, nor hermaphrodite,
> Not a girl, nor young woman, nor aged,
> Neither chaste, nor vicious, nor fruitful,
> BUT ALL.
> She was buried, not through famine, nor iron sword,
> Nor poison, but through all.
> Neither in heaven nor earth, nor in water
> does she lie, but EVERYWHERE she rests.
>
> LUCIUS AGATHO PRISCUS,
> Not husband, not lover, nor dear friend,
> Not mourning, not rejoicing, not knowing,
> For what this is
> Not mound, not pyramid, not sepulchre
> But all of them.

All and nothing here placed
For certain this is a tomb,
Cadaver it holds not
Neither does the dead body contain the tomb
This is the Sepulchre.

Once again we are reminded of the ancient *Tabula Smaragdina*: 'What is above is equal to that which is below, and What is below is equal to that above.' So the two supposed inscriptions equate opposites and confuse them into a unity which is irrational.

No wonder that old philosophers loved the tantalizing little poetic riddle!

In China alchemy had passed from the comparison and confection of jade to gold, and then to a concentration on the personality of the adept. The spiritual transmutation became the main aim of the student of the mysteries of alchemy. One gathers the impression that a native belief had been influenced by ideas coming from the West, especially through the Manichaeans, which were absorbed and then became a path of perfection. The concept was very closely associated with Taoist belief. Arthur Waley's translation of the book of the travels of the Taoist Ch'ang-Chun includes one little poem showing an identity of philosophical thought with the western alchemical world:

A temporary compound of the Four Elements
The body at last must suffer decay.
The soul, composed of one spiritual essence
Is free to move wherever it will.[1]

This little poem stopped a project for the removal of the bones of a holy man from his burial place.

The European alchemists were never able to express themselves with the clarity of the Chinese sage, mostly because they were more sharply aware of the complex relationship between alchemy and their formal religious beliefs. Their innate urge to define and explain conflicted with the rule that the secrets must not be thrown open to everyone. In an effort to define the teacher Thoth (Ṭehuti), they refer to him as the 'first man'. We find that Zosimus describes him as the interpreter who had given names to all created things, and who is named by Chaldeans, Parthians, Medes and Hebrews as Adam. He goes on to say: 'So the first Man is called by us Thyoth and by them Adam, which is a name in the language of the Angels: but with

[1] *The Travels of an Alchemist: recorded by his Disciple Li Chih-Chang*, translated with an introduction by Arthur Waley (Routledge and Kegan Paul, London 1931 and 1964).

reference to his body they named him with reference to the four elements of the Heavenly Sphere.'[1]

The religious aspect becomes clearer in Byzantine days, when we have the advice given by the Orthodox hermit Morienus to the devout Mohammedan student Prince Khalid:

The thing for which you have sought so long is not to be acquired or accomplished by force or passion. It is only to be won by patience and humility and by a determined and most perfect love. For God bestows this divine and immaculate science on his faithful servants, namely on those whom He resolved to bestow it from the original nature of things.

... Nor were the elect able to hold anything back save through the strength granted to them by God, and they themselves could no longer direct their minds save towards the goal appointed for them by God. For God charges those of his servants whom he has purposely chosen that they seek this divine science which is hidden from men, and that they keep it to themselves. This is the science that draws its master away from the suffering of this world and leads to the knowledge of future good.

When Morienus was asked by the King why he lived in mountains and deserts rather than in hermitages, he answered 'I do not doubt that in Hermitages and Brotherhoods I would find greater repose, and fatiguing work in the mountains and deserts; but no one reaps who does not sow. The Gateway to peace is exceeding narrow, and none may enter save through the suffering of the soul'.[2]

We shall find this theme repeated and echoed in all alchemical literature. The emphasis is equally on the state of mind of the adept, and on the material work of the transmutation. But there was always the danger that the experimental side of the art might be discovered by unfit persons. Hence elaborate omissions and deceptions were included in the text. Various materials were described under false names. In what follows, the *materia prima*, the essential material of the universe, is described as the serpent. This serpent is put in an alchemical vessel and the four elements are divided from it, so the description says it is in a chariot driven by its four wheels. It is all made into a strange story, which yet has a certain beauty in its skilled construction.

The source is *Tractatus Aristotelis ad Alexandrum Magnum olim conscriptus et a quondam Christiano Philosopho Collectus.*

Take the serpent and place it in the chariot with four wheels and let it be turned

[1] C. G. Jung: *Collected Works*, Vol. 12, *Psychology and Alchemy*, pp. 349–50. (Routledge and Kegan Paul, London 1953).
[2] *ibid.* p. 260.

# The Seventeenth Century: Later Work

Portrait of Sir Kenelm Digby (1603–65), English alchemist and philosopher

The First Key from Basilius Valentinus: *Practica una cum duodecim clavibus*. The King and Queen between death and animality

The Second Key: Mercurius as the uniting symbol

The Third Key: The dragon in the earthly sphere

The Fourth Key: The Nigredo or Putrefactio

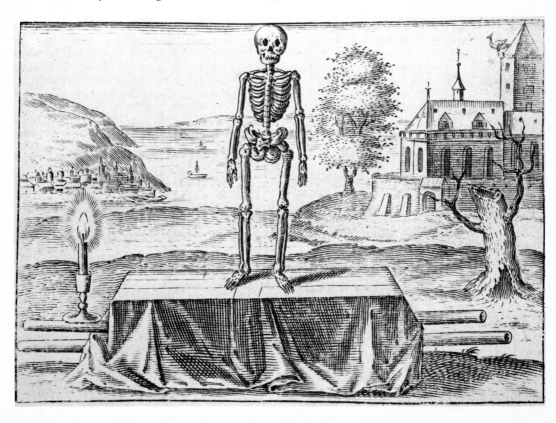

The Fifth Key: The Solar Lion and the elements inspired by love

The Sixth Key: The King and Queen united and the furnaces of union

The Seventh Key: The materials in their season are enclosed in Chaos

The Eighth Key: The Resurrection is the target of the Adepts

The Ninth Key: The Triad forms a unity supporting the duality
which develops the spiritual quaternity

The Tenth Key: The Sun, Moon and Mercury in symbols of holiness

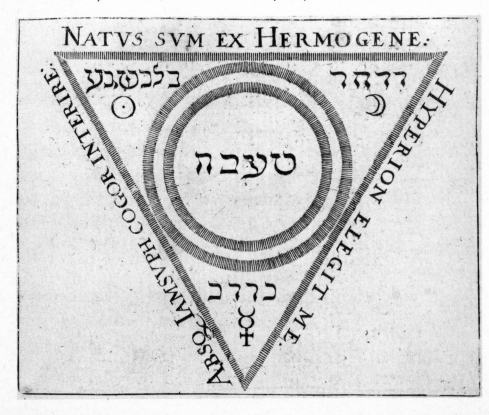

The Eleventh Key: The twins Sun and Moon are united by the conjunction
which seems to be death

The Twelfth Key: Unity is achieved in the golden flower

Conyng
Experience
Pracktike
Prudent
Pacience

Gras
Nature
Reson
Spekelatiue
Holi lifing

# HERMES BIRD.

**P**roblemis of olde likenes and fuguris,
Wych proved byn fructuos of sentens;
And have auctorite grounded in Scripture,
By resemblaunce of notabil apperence;
Wych moralites concludyng on prudence:
Lyke as the Bibel reherseth be wryting,
How Trees sum tyme chese hemselfe a Kyng.

First page of Lully's *Hermes Bird*. The dragon inspirited from above becomes the tree of the philosophers

Final page and vignette of *Liber Patris Sapientiae*, showing the dragon arising from the *massa confusa*

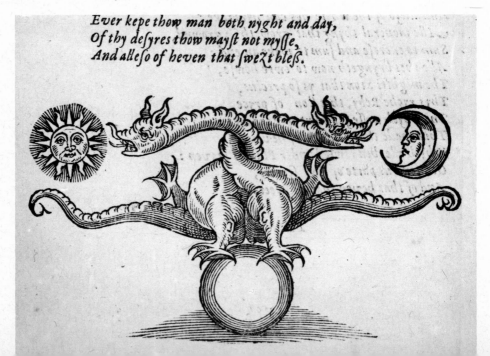

Ever kepe thow man both nyght and day,
Of thy desyres thow mayst not mysse,
And alleso of heven that sweȝt bless.

about on the earth until it is immersed in the depths of the sea, and nothing more is visible but the blackest Dead Sea. And there let the chariot with the wheels remain, until so many fumes rise up from the serpent that the whole flat surface becomes dry and by dessication sandy and black. All that is the earth which is no earth, but a stone lacking all weight. . . . and when the vapour is precipitated like rain . . . you should bring the chariot from water to dry land, and then you have placed the four wheels on the chariot, and will obtain the result if you will advance further to the Red Sea, running without running, moving without motion.[1]

This confusion continues until the sixteenth century, and is in fact so openly employed as to allow of a certain humour when describing it. The following, from Eirenaeus's *Marrow of Alchemy*, is a pleasing example:

### Hunting the Greene Lyon

All hail to the noble companie
Of students in holi Alkimie;
Whose noble practise doth them teach
To veil their art wyth mysty speech;
Mought it please your worshipfulnes,
To hear my idle soothfastnes,
Of that stronge practise I have seene,
In hunting of the Lyon Greene,
Whose colour doubtless ys not soe
As that your wisdom well doe know;
For no man lives that ere hath seene
Upon foure feet a lyon greene,
But our lyon wanting maturitie,
Is called greene for his unripenes trust me,
And yet full quickly he can run
And soon can overtake the Sun;
And suddenly can hym devoure . . .

Here there is a double deception which is no deception, for the Green Lion is very acid and not really unripe. It is *aqua fortis* which can dissolve gold, and is in fact a mixed acid with a greenish tinge in its colour. So Eirenaeus is being clear enough to his fellow scientists and yet very confusing and amusing to the ordinary run of readers.

It was possible in the erudite culture of the early sixteenth century for Melchior Cibinensis to make a poetic description of the whole business of the transmutation in terms which the adept might have found only

[1] *ibid.* p. 202.

moderately obscure, but which is really beyond the skill of people not steeped in the ritual of the alchemical art.

Hail beautiful lamp of heaven, shining light of the world. Here thou art united with the moon, here ariseth the bond of Mars, and the conjunction with Mercury. From these there is born through the magistery of the art, in the river bed, the strong giant whom a thousand times a thousand seek, when these three shall have dissolved not into rain water ... but into mercurial water, into this our blessed gum which dissolves of itself and is named the Sperm of the Philosophers. Now he makes haste to bind and betroth himself to the virgin bride, and to get her with child in the bath of a moderate fire. But the virgin becometh not pregnant at once unless she be kissed in repeated embraces. Then she conceives in her body, and thus is begotten the child of good omen, in accordance with the order of nature. Then will appear in the bottom of the vessel the mighty Ethiopian, burned, calcined, bleached, altogether dead and lifeless. He asks to be buried, to be sprinkled with his own moisture and slowly calcined until he shall arise in glowing form from the fierce fire ... Behold a wondrous restoration or renewal of the Ethiopian! Because of the bath of rebirth he takes a new name, which the Philosophers call the Natural Sulphur and their son, this being the Stone of the Philosophers. And behold it is *one* thing, *one* root, *one* essence with nothing extraneous added and from which much that was superfluous is taken away by the magistery of the art. . . . It is the Treasure of Treasures, the supreme Philosophical Potion, the Divine Secret of the ancients. Blessed is he that finds such a thing.

One that has seen this thing writes and speaks openly, and I know that his testimony is true. Praise be to God for evermore![1]

This phraseology conceals a great mystery, but rather clearly. Fantastically the old alchemist thought he was composing a paraphrase of the beautiful hymn *Salve Regina*. Probably this intimates that he was so deeply involved with his work that he felt the Divine blessing all around him. It was as wonderful as the mystery of the Incarnation. The essential unity of the worlds of Spirit and of nature were demonstrated before him. Sun and moon are united in the bond of Mars with Mercury by amalgamation in a very strong closed vessel. The product is heated and turns into a black substance which is heated until vapours rise and condense. (Mercury must here mean something different from normal mercury or we should have no black *nigredo* phase.) Then a new substance is added, this gum named the 'Sperm of the Philosophers' (later works describe a golden-coloured distillate which may be the material described). Further silver is added and the process of heating and condensing continues in a water bath so that the heat shall be easily regulated. The 'child' is a crystalline substance, but at the

[1] *ibid.* pp. 384–386.

end of the process only the black ash is left. Heat is increased and the black becomes red and glows, changing finally to a pale powder which they term the 'Sulphur of the Philosophers'. And this is the mysterious Philosopher's Stone by which powers that seem to be miraculous are bestowed upon its owner.

In our scientific age the experiment has been repeated with some success, as we shall see later. Of course the same kind of secrecy and confusion of ideas are used by the modern alchemists. The result is still scientifically impossible with the means used, though there is evidence on a very small scale that a few experimenters have achieved the scientifically impossible. But for many adepts the personal transmutation was something of far greater importance. The philosophy of the modern world has aimed at integration of the whole man, with its strange concomitant experience of the unity of the living world with the individual at a very deep level. The two paths seem to be open. But that is for later discussion.

First we might do well to return to one of the great minds of the Middle Ages to give greater authority to the writing – Albertus Magnus, quoted in the *Theatrum Chemicum*. This work is the *Liber octo capitulorum de lapide philosophorum*. The author is talking about the Mercury of the philosophers:

Quicksilver is cold and moist and God created all minerals with it, and it is itself aerial and volatile in the fire. (That is it contains the Four Elements). Since it withstands the fire for some time it will do great and wonderful work, and it alone is a living spirit, and in all the world there is nothing like it that can do such things. . . . It is the perennial water, the water of life, the virgin's milk, the fount, the alumen, and whoever drinks of it shall not perish. When it is alive it does certain works, and when it is dead it does other and the greatest works. It is the serpent that rejoices in itself, impregnates itself and gives birth in a single day, and slays all metals with its venom. It flees from the fire, but the sages by their art have caused it to withstand the fire, by nourishing it with its own earth until it endured the fire, and then it performs works and transmutations.

Later the writer continues:

Our final secret consists in this, that one obtains the medicine which flows, before Mercurius evaporates. . . . There is no worthier nor proper substance than the Sun and its shadow the Moon, without which no tincturing quicksilver can be produced. . . . He who understands therefore how to unite this with the Sun or Moon will obtain the arcanum, which is named the Sulphur of the Art.

Our stone is of watery nature, because it is cold and moist. For such a disposition of the body is considered obvious or manifest. But breadth is the middle disposition whereby depth is obtained. This is the medium between breadth and depth as between two extremes or opposites, and the passage from one opposite to another and from one extreme to the other is impossible save by a medium disposition. Because the stone is cold and moist.[1]

Here the writer is not only telling of the mysterious 'philosophical mercury', but introducing some strange ideas about the dimension between breadth and depth. The idea has some connection with the favourite name for alchemy in the seventeenth and eighteenth centuries, the spagiric art, the art of far and near, or centrifugal and centripetal energy. This idea has ancient, even prehistoric, roots in the thought of the breath of life coming into this world through the woman's womb, and leaving through the magical womb of earth, the grave. To and from, from and to, the constant moving from one condition to another leads us to the alchemists' idea of the meaning of Above and Below in the *Tabula Smaragdina* as different dimensional constructions of space. The lower worlds have greater densities and lesser dimensions; the higher are more ethereal and light and are larger.

Gerhard Dorn, in the sixteenth century, tells us:

The caelum (the Stone) therefore is a heavenly substance and a universal form, containing in itself all forms, distinct from one another but proceeding from one single universal form. Wherefore he who knows how individuals can be led on to the most general genus by the spagiric art, and how the special virtues, one or more, can be impressed upon this genus will easily find the universal medicine. ... For since there is one single and most general beginning of all corruptions, and one universal fount of regenerating, restoring, and life-giving virtues, who save a man bereft of his senses, will call such a medicine in doubt?[2]

This talk is clearly seen by Dorn to be incomprehensible to his readers; yet it contains philosophic ideas of considerable importance, which are now expressed in different phrases than in the ancient world. He is putting more clearly the idea that the wonderful arcane substance of alchemy is a universal substance which transcends time and space. This is a vital point in all mystery religions and is undoubtedly of ancient origin, but Dorn has fitted it into the thought of his period and returned much of alchemical mysticism to the realm of philosophy.

Between the philosophic thought of Dorn and the romantic pictorial mysteries which form so many of our illustrations falls the paper on *Experience and Philosophy* in Elias Ashmole's *Theatrum Chemicum*, p. 336:

One thing was first employed,
Which shall not be destroyed:

[1] C. G. Jung: *Collected Works*, Vol. 14. *Mysterium Conjunctionis*, pp. 478, 479 (Routledge and Kegan Paul, London 1963).
[2] *ibid.* p. 479.

It compasseth the world so round,
A matter easy to be found:
And yet most hard to come by.
A secret of secrets pardye,
That is most vile and least set by,
But it's my Love and Darling,
Conceived with all living thing,
And travels to the world's ending.
A child begetting his own Father, and bearing hys Mother,
Killing himself to give life and light to all other,
    Is that I meane,
Most mild and most extreme.
Did not the world that dwelt in me
Take form and walk forth visibly;
And did not I then dwell in It,
That dwelt in me for to unite,
Three Powers in one seat to sit.

Here we find again the alchemical philosophy is on the same line as Christian theology. It was quite early in its history that a system of spiritual contemplation of chemistry evolved, and was linked with many Christian heresies and with a form of Mohammedan belief. So there is nothing strange in this post-Reformation appearance of the ancient ideas linked with new philosophies. One feels this strongly at the beginning of Norton's *Ordinall of Alchemy*, in which the science is apostrophized as a being with some kind of personal quality almost as if it were an angel, and yet under the control of an adept who must preserve great personal purity of motive, for fear of the consequences to all the world. So one must treat this science as something holy. Here are Norton's words:

Mais tryeful, merveylous, and Archimastrye
Is the tincture of holi Alkimy;
A wonderful science and secret filosophy
A singular grace and gift of the Almightye;
Which never was found, as witness we can,
Nor thys science was ever taught to man,
But he were probed perfectly with space,
Whether he were able to receive this grace.
For his trewth, virtue and for his stable wit,
Which if he faill, he shall never have it.
ALSO NO MAN SHOULD THIS SCIENCE TEACH

173

For it is so wonderful and so selcouth,
That it must needs be taught fro mouth to mouth;
Also he must (if he be never so loath),
Receive it with a most sacred oath,
That, as we refuse great dignity and fame,
Soe he must needly refuse the same.
And this Science must ever secret be,
The cause whereof is this, as ye may see,
If one evil man had hereof all his will,
All Christian Peace he might easily spill;
And with his pride he might pull downe,
Rightful Kings and Princes of renowne;
Wherefore the sentence of peril and jeopardy
Upon the teacher resteth dreadfully.

So that for doubt of such pride and wealth
He must beware that will this science teach,
No man therefore may reach this present
But he has virtues excellent.

So tho men weene possessors not to aide
To hallow this science as before is saide,
Neither seem not blessed effectually,
Yet, in her order, this science is holy.
And forasmuch as no man may her find
But only by grace, she is holy in her kind.
Also it is a work and cure divine,
Foul copper to make gold and silver fine;
No man may find such change by his thought,
Of divers kinds which God's hands have wroughte;
For God's conjunctions man may not undoe,
But if His grace fully consent thereto,
By help of this science, which our Lord above,
Has given to such men as He doth love,
Wherefore old Fathers, conveniently,
Called this Science Holy Alkimy.

There is our warning clear and without equivocation. If we seek to uncover this secret, or teach it with material gain and power as our motive, it is likely to destroy us. Those old philosophers seem to have had some ideas about human nature which we should do well to remember. In their time they had reason to think about such things because these works were written at the period of the Thirty Years' War, an idea of which is given in Brecht's play *Mother Courage*. Alchemy or the truths which were behind it can only be properly used if mankind really decides to seek the paths of peace. And that is a non-alchemical idea going back some two thousand years in the West.

From this point we may consider the actual relationship of the alchemists' ideas to empirical science. There is not any rational connection to be observed, for they thought differently from us. The best of them were willing to spend tens of years in a series of experiments which gradually led them to the point where enlightenment dawned on them. Then almost invariably they say that the secret was so simple that it was almost immediately clear to them. Yet they never regretted their long years of servitude to the art. To them it was absolutely necessary that the individual should seek and find the path little by little. The philosopher, Heinrich Khunrath, depicted the path as being separated from the pleasures and temptations of this world. This was followed by the entry into a long dark cavern, which was lit by hope and yet was so dark that one might well despair. In the end one came into a fair land within which was a fortress. Before the fortress were many chambers, one of which could be the entrance. Many seekers tried these entrances but gave up, unsuccessful. The few found the main entrance through a narrow gateway over a perilous moat. Once they were over they had to pass an examination and face ordeals to prove their character before they might enter the fortress and find the path which led to Paradise.

As Professor Jung has pointed out so insistently, we may all find these paths of experience open to us, in that great world of the unconscious which is within us and which links us to the whole of nature. The adventures are strangely parallel to normal dream sequences which we pass through in our pilgrimage through life. The result, if we pass through properly, is integration of the whole personality. We realize the totality of our being, which is indeed a worthwhile pilgrimage. The modern psychologist and the old-time adept understood the path of human development, though in different ways. The alchemist in the earlier days projected all these events into his exterior world, and used the discipline of the laboratory as a vehicle for daydreams. It is not the total story, for there are a few points of confusion which no one has adequately cleared up. However, at this point we should do well to look at some of the stories of the material process of transmutation as the adepts saw it.

Here is a seventeenth-century report by George Starkey (as reprinted by

James Elliott & Co, 1893) from *The Stone of the Philosophers: Embracing
the First Matter and the Dual Process for the Vegetable and Metallic Tinctures:*

... All true Philosophers agree that the first matter of metals is a moist vapour,
raised by the action of the central fire in the bowels of the earth, which, circulating
through its pores, meets with the crude air, and is coagulated by it into an unctuous
water, adhering to the earth, which serves it for a receptacle, where it is joined
to a sulphur more or less pure, and a salt more or less fixing, which it attracts from
the air, and receiving a certain degree of concoction from the central and solar
heat, is formed into stones and rocks, minerals and metals. ...

Gems are in like manner formed of this moist vapour when it meets pure salt
water, with which it is fixed in a cold place. But if it is sublimed leisurely through
places which are hot and pure, where the fatness of sulphur adheres to it, this
vapour which the Philosophers call their Mercury, is joined to that fatness and
becomes an unctuous matter, which coming upward to other places cleansed by
the aforenamed vapours, where the earth is subtle, pure and moist, fills the pores
of it, and so gold is made.

This may be described as the argument from volcanoes; but it gave the
alchemist a backing of what appeared to be observational science for his
work in the laboratory.

All philosophers affirm, with one consent, that metals have a seed by which they
are increased, and that this seminal quality is the same in all of them; but it is
perfectly ripened in gold only, where the bond of union is so fixed that it is
difficult to decompound the subject, and procure it for the Philosophical Work.
But some who were adepts in the art, have by painful processes taken gold for
their male, and the mercury, which they knew how to extract from the less
compacted metals, for a female; not as an easier process but to find out the
possibility of making the Stone this way; and have succeeded, giving the method
more openly to conceal the true confection, which is more easy and simple.

This is traditional knowledge coming from quite ancient speculation about
the nature of metals, linked with ideas about the production of amalgams
which go back to the goldsmiths in Alexandria. But this is all brought into a
later, more advanced routine. The alchemist puts his materials through many
more processes. We next see how the final steps of the process result in the
appearance of a marvellous elixir which has powers beyond reason.

... Our vessel being warily heated at the first for fear of its cracking, an ebulli-
tion of the contained matter is brought on, so that the moisture is alternately
circulated in white fumes above and condensed below, which may continue for a
month or two, nay, longer, increasing the heat gradually to another degree, as
your matter discovers a disposition for fixing, by the vapour continuing at longer

*Folio 29 from* Splendor Solis

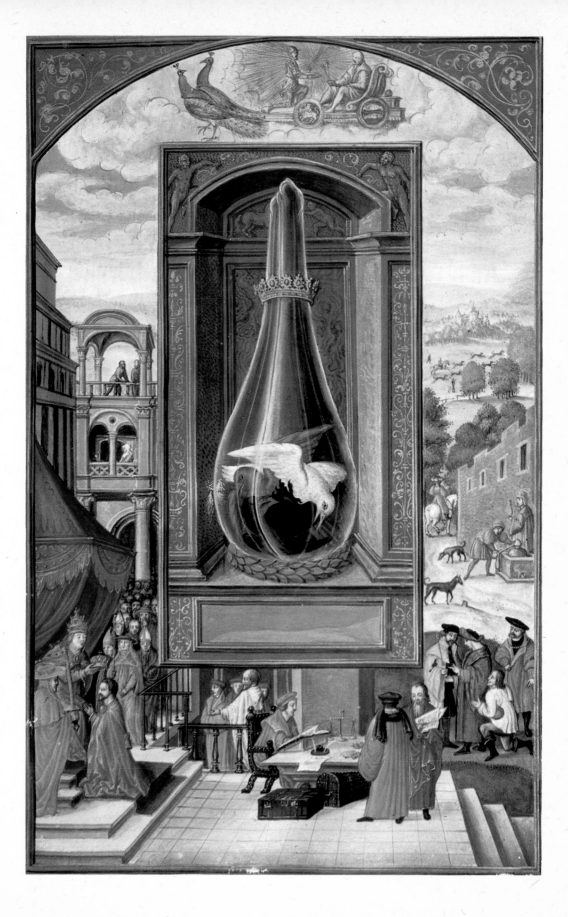

intervals condensed, and rising in a lesser quantity of an ash colour, or other dark shades which it will assume as a medium to perfect blackness, the first desirable stage in our harvest. Other colours may be exhibited in this part of the work without danger, if they pass transiently; but if a faint redness like that of the corn poppy, continues the matter is in danger of vitrifying. . . .

This has all been going on in a hermetically sealed vessel with no addition to the original contents; but we are told that at this danger point the adept may add more of the 'actuated mercury' and reseal the vessel.

. . . after they have continued for some time at rest a pellicle or film on the matter shows its disposition for fixing, retaining the vapour captive for some time till it breaks through at different places on its surface (much like the bituminous substance of coal in a soldering fire), with darker clouds, but quickly dissipated, and growing less in quantity, till the whole substance resembles molten pitch, or the aforesaid bituminous substance, bubbling less and less, resting in one entire black substance at the bottom of your glass. This is called the blackness of black, the head of the crow, etc., and is esteemed a desirable stage in our philosophical generation, being the perfect putrefaction of our seed, which will ere long show its vital principle by a glorious manifestation of Seminal Virtue.

Here we find the Head of the Crow and enter on descriptions which the reader will find echoed in the illustrations.

Chapter XI: A further description of the Process.

When the putrefaction has been thus completed, the fire may be increased till glorious colours appear, which the Sons of Art have called the Cauda Pavonis, or the Peacock's Tail. These colours come and go, as heat is administered approaching to the third degree till all is of a beautiful green, and as it ripens assumes a perfect whiteness, which is the White Tincture, transmuting the inferior metals into silver, and very powerful as a medicine. But as the artist well knows it is capable of a higher concoction, he goes on increasing his fire till it assumes a yellow, then an orange or citron colour; and then boldly gives it a heat of the fourth degree, till it acquires a redness like blood taken from a sound person, which is a manifest sign of its thorough concoction and fitness for the uses intended.

Chapter XII: of the Stone and its Uses.

Having thus completed the operation, let the vessel cool, and on opening it you will perceive your matter to be fixed into a ponderous mass, thoroughly of a scarlet colour, which is easily reducible to powder by scraping, or otherwise, and in being heated in the fire flows like wax, without smoking, flaming or loss of substance, returning when cold to its former fixity, heavier than gold bulk for bulk, yet easy to be dissolved in any liquid, in which a few grains being taken its operation most wonderfully pervades the human body, to the extirpation of all disorders, prolonging life by its use to its utmost period; and hence it has obtained the appelation of 'Panacea' or a universal remedy. Therefore be thankful to the Most High for the possession of such an inestimable jewel, and account the possession of it not as the result of your own ingenuity, but a gift bestowed of God's mere bounty, for the relief of human infirmities. . . .

We are here warned not to deny the use of the Panacea, but to be careful to preserve the stone from the vicious and unworthy. The description given here of the process seems to have been recorded more than once in similar terms. The mysterious red powder is frequently mentioned, and is prominent in the story of Nicolas Flamel. Here we have the strange description of its qualities and of its great specific gravity. This belongs to a world of non-science as far as we can see, yet it poses a mystery for there is an element of reason in its weight which is apparent to us, if not to the alchemists. If their accounts are true we are reading the description of a very strange form of matter.

Chapter XIII: Of the Transmutation.

It is much to be lamented that the seekers of natural knowledge in this art propose, principally, the Science of Transmutation as their ultimate view, and overlooking the chief excellency of our Stone as a medicine. Notwithstanding this grovelling spirit, we shall commit the issue to His Providence, and declare the Transmutation (which indeed the Philosophers do) openly, after which we shall describe the further circulation of our Stone for its virtues, and then make an end of our treatise.

When the artist would transmute any metal – for instance lead – let a quantity be melted in a clean crucible, to which let a few grains of gold in filings be cast; and when the whole is melted, let him have in readiness a little of the powder, which will easily scrape off from his Stone, the quantity inconsiderable, and cast it on the metal while in fusion. Immediately there will arise a thick fume which carries off with it the impurities contained within the lead, with a crackling noise, and leaves the substance of the lead transmuted into most pure gold, without any kind of sophistication; the small quantity of gold added, previous to projection, serves only as a medium to facilitate the transmutation, and the quantity of your tincture is best ascertained by experience, as its virtue is proportioned to the number of circulations you have given after the first has been completed.

For instance: when you have finished the Stone, dissolve it in our mercury again, wherein you have previously dissolved a few grains of pure gold. This operation is done without trouble, both substances readily liquefying. Put it into your vessel as before, and go through the process. There is no danger in the management but breaking your vessel; and every time it is thus treated its virtues are increased, in a ratio of ten to one hundred, a thousand, ten thousand, etc., both in medicinal and transmuting qualities; so that a small quantity may suffice for the purposes of an artist during the remaining term of his life.

This account fits in well with the description given by Helvetius, except that he was not told to add a few grains of gold to his molten lead. It is not a rational procedure, yet the traditional nature of the information is quite strong for it is very close to the instructions given in the *Bosom Book* of Sir George Ripley, Canon of Bridlington, nearly two centuries earlier.

The works of Basilius Valentinus, who was probably a monk living in Thuringia in East Germany, tell of the same quest, but he is concerned with the extraction of liquid forms of the stone, using antimony. His period appears to belong to the early sixteenth century since one of the important uses of the elixir is as a cure for venereal disease which had been recently introduced into Europe. The work is a devout religious treatise, and his aim is not transmutation but the preparation of medicines in which the philosopher's stone appears as a liquid of such great healing powers that he considers it to be the panacea for all ailments. Expressing another view, but of the same school of thought, Basil found his *materia prima* in antimony. Nevertheless he notes the possibility of obtaining from other substances results of equal value but with slightly differing characteristics.

This older alchemical literature has a mass of difficulties for us because we do not see the problem in the same terms. The four elements of the alchemists remain only in the domain of poetic symbolism; the terms for the materials used and the processes are hard to comprehend without considerable research. Scientifically we do not speak the same language at all. The tendency for alchemical thought to turn into philosophical speculation was as inevitable in Europe as it had been a thousand years earlier in China. It pursued the same course towards expression in religious symbolism. An early stage of this change of attitude is to be found in the early Rosicrucian ideas, which have a very definite tinge of alchemical thought. In fact two great men of the seventeenth century, Michael Maier, the German alchemist, and Elias Ashmole, the English philosopher, founder of the Ashmolean Museum and publisher of a fine collection of alchemical works, were associated with Rosicrucian ideals. Some of Maier's work may be found in the illustrations. He had a great gift for pictorial expression. Ashmole was very interested in the Rosicrucians, and tried to link their ritual with the Mysteries of Greece and Rome. He made his collection of alchemical texts as part of a projected larger work. However, he became a close associate of an alchemical philosopher, William Backhouse, who communicated to him the inner secret of the *materia prima*, which was the basic material from which the philosopher's stone was to be prepared. Ashmole notes the fact. The date was 13 May 1653. From that day to his death in 1692 Ashmole wrote nothing to do with alchemy. Whether the secret was so clear that he felt no need to pursue the matter scientifically, or whether it was an exposition of the spiritual nature of the quest in which the *materia prima* is no material at all, we do not know.

It may be that the matter was similar to the philosophy of Khunrath who was in close contact with Michael Maier. Perhaps we have a clue in the Rosicrucian canons associated with Benedict Hilarion, who in 1622 was quoting the following on the subject of alchemy:

1. That metals and other minerals are found only in mountains and under earth of Salt, Sulphur and Mercury;
2. That this earth is impregnated by Nature with mineral water;
3. That whilst the metals grow undisturbed the root of all metals comes forth;
4. That this is the First Matter of all the wise, whom God has made glad by knowledge of the Most High Mastery of Nature;
5. That the virtue of this nature is in the body, that is, in Salt, which Salt or the body maintains the Sulphur and Mercury, otherwise spirit and soul with itself;
6. That the matter of Highest Mastery is found in fire and water or in impregnated water, which water is not moist and does not wet the fingers;
7. That all things are one thing only;
8. That this water cannot abide without earth, which earth nourished fire and air by the active Spirit of the Creator;
9. That there is a perpetual intercourse of the Divine Essence with created bodies;
10. That the Divine Essence is manifested through fire and water, as through Spirit and Soul:
11. That Created things are brought forth and manifested by earth and water, as through bodies:
12. That herein lies the sacrament and mystery of the correspondence between the philosophical work of highest science and the harmony of the Sacrosaintly Divine Trinity, even as Ergon with Parergon. Glory unto God alone.[1]

Here we must take our leave of the ancient writings of the alchemists. They have enjoyed and expounded their mystery. It has altered somewhat in time, just as the apparatus used in the experimental work has altered. The still has replaced the *kerotakis*, and the secret philosopher has replaced the assembly of the Mysteries. It would seem that, by the eighteenth century, alchemy was doomed.

The survival in obscure places is however to be noted. It may be that no further advance will be made. Even in the beginning of the nineteenth century we had the tragic story from Stoke D'Abernon of the experiments and final suicide of James Price. It was not the end of the experimental story but marked the break with science for at least a century and a half.

[1] A.E.Waite: *The Brotherhood of the Rosy Cross.* (London, 1924; reprint: University Books, New York, 1961).

When making enquiries in the Department of Coins and Medals at the British Museum the author was shown some fine reproductions of the alchemical medals of the eighteenth century, and a strange specimen of apparently unworked gold. It looks like a twig, one end having a crystal shaped fracture, and the other showing small holes as if gas had blown through the metal when it was molten. Its weight shows it to be of the specific gravity of gold. On it is a label of the type used some eighty years ago, saying that this is a specimen of so-called alchemical gold. There is a reference to a further note preserved in a scrapbook. Unfortunately that scrapbook with some other documents was kept in a safe in the Department and was destroyed on the tragic night during the last war when incendiary bombs set fire to the old offices. The safe remained but it had been subjected to such a temperature that a silver vessel inside had become a misshapen ingot, and the papers were a mist of white ash. So we have no real record of the origin of the strange little fragment of gold. One knows from the label that it was an old specimen, but from there it is pure guesswork. Since Sir Joseph Banks was a great friend of the British Museum and gave many things of natural history and ethnography to the collections, one may be permitted to wonder whether this was perhaps given to the National Collection by Sir Joseph Banks as a specimen of the gold which James Price claimed to have manufactured. But it is only a guess. In any case this is a tiny fragment and its history is lost. It is not a final proof of any kind, but naturally its existence is of interest to scientists.

Perhaps to us the alchemical coins and the piece of gold are the important exceptions, the few objective and material pieces of evidence among a mass of confused documents, deliberate falsifications, and accounts of charlatanry which would put a modern confidence trickster to shame. If they are genuine products of a process of alchemical experiment as described by the ancient authorities quoted above, they are inexplicable by our modern knowledge. They must belong to a curious world of mysticism which includes the appearance of solid objects as part of its procedure. If they are the results of the experiment only when made by a purified personality there seems as little chance of repeating the experiment success-fully now as at any time in the past. Although there seem to be about half a dozen cases of making alchemical gold which are properly recorded we must remember that in these few examples we have spanned three centuries. Every story has elements which would identify it with the nature of a dream series. Every record makes it clear that the true alchemist had experienced great psychological development and realized that the most terrible evils would follow a revelation of the secret. This was so strongly felt that death was preferred to betrayal of the divine secret. It is obvious that the search for the alchemical secret was most unrewarding. We have only to note that nearly all the sincere researchers spent most of their manhood seeking in vain, and that the clue was only given to them in later years. There was very little to tempt even the adept to go far. One could not become an adept without having renounced nearly all human sensations. The ego had to be thoroughly subdued before the *persona* could be realized. So the successful alchemist was without greed, and either performed good works, like Flamel, or devoted his wisdom to medicine like Basilius Valentinus. Some eighteenth-century alchemists made gold for kings and died in lonely dungeons, while the gold was spent on the brutalities of war. It is not a profitable or tempting way of life.

# 13

# GolD from the Blackness

More than a century after the publication of Mary Anne Atwood's book, the last dated document mentioned so far, the author was having supper with some friends and was advised to read a book by C.R. Cammell, FRSA.[1] In it there was an account of an alchemist who had lived in England, worked in Surrey and spent his last few years at Eastbourne, where he died in the present decade. Certainly the chapter was very carefully written and most convincing. Mr Cammell, a trained and exact observer, had seen his friend Archibald Cockren engaged in a successful experiment in the use of the ancient alchemical techniques. His account is more succinct than that in Archibald Cockren's own words, but the inescapable fact is that, for a period of half a year, he watched a 'crystal' of gold grow like a plant of the cactus type – the earlier specimen in the British Museum is like a twig – from a black mass in a hermetically sealed vessel in Cockren's laboratory. This must have been in the nineteen-fifties. Mr Cammell makes a very apt comparison of what is to follow in a quotation from Paracelsus (Theophrastus Bombastus) which appears in *Of the Nature of Things*, Lib. II, (London, 1650).

It is possible also that Gold, through industry and skill of an expert Alchymist may bee so far exalted, that it may grow in a glasse like a tree, with many wonderfull boughs, and leaves, which indeed is pleasant to behold, and most wonderfull.

There follows with a marginal rubric thus: 'How the Philosophicall Tree is made':

The process is this. Let Gold be calcined with *Aqua Regis*, till it becomes a kind of chalke, which put into a gourd glasse, and pour upon it good new *Aqua Regis*, so that it may cover it foure fingers breadth, then againe draw it off, with the third degree of fire, untill no more ascend. The water that is distilled off poure on

---

[1] *Heart of Scotland* (Robert Hale, London 1956).

183

againe, then distill it off againe. This doe so long untill thou seest the gold to rise in the glasse, and grow after the manner of a tree, having many boughs and leaves; and so there is made by gold a wonderful and pleasant shrub, which the Alchymists call their Golden Hearbe, and the Philosophers' Tree. In like manner you may proceed with silver, and other metalls, yet soe that their calcination be made after another manner, by another *Aqua Fortis*, which I leave to thine experience. If thou art skilled in Alchymie, thou shalt not erre in these things.

This reads like a pleasant demonstration for a pastime: dissolve some gold in *aqua regia*, then heat the crystals formed in the solution until a white amorphous powder results; purify with more acid, dry out again, and gently heat. The result will be that the particles of gold in the compound will separate and slowly coalesce in a form apparently like a tree of 'crystals' of pure gold. Cockren's own account is much more complete and less simple; in fact he goes further than Paracelsus, as we shall see:

Cockren was a man with scientific training. His professional field, in which he reached high distinction, was massage. He performed distinguished service in a medical unit in the war of 1914–18, and was one of the leading pioneers of electro massage. His friends, some of whom are still living, are of the opinion that he was an intelligent, straightforward man who had the courage to experiment in an obscure and practically discredited field. They say he was incapable of intentional falsehood. His work is clear and simple. In his book *Alchemy Rediscovered and Restored* (1940) he discusses ancient authorities and recalls a tradition that the original Hermes Trismegistus worked in Egypt about 1900 BC, in the reign of Sesostris (Usertesen) II, of the great Twelfth Dynasty, and was coeval with the earlier phase of Stonehenge in Britain. His note of Diocletian's destruction of Egyptian alchemical works in 296 AD explains much later confusion. He includes some useful translations of the book of Nicolas Flamel and from Comte de St Germain. He places the alchemical quintessence in the following equation: astral light = imponderable ether = the quintessence = electricity = Vedic *prana*. He was well acquainted with both science and esoteric philosophy of his own day, as well as having a very thorough knowledge of the ancient works of the alchemists. But he warns us that it is imperative for adepts to remember that the secret must be kept. So, although his outlook is modern, he preserves the secret of the material which he used as the *materia prima*. He is attracted, like Basilius Valentinus, to the thought of alchemy as primarily a medical process. He follows Robert Vaughan with particular care. So his philosophical approach was associated with repetition of the ancient experiments. He had considerable advantages over his predecessors, since he was able to use good laboratory glassware which would withstand

# The Eighteenth Century and After

The salamander: vignette from the title-page of volume II of the *Bibliotheca Chemica Curiosa*, 1702

Illustrations of apparatus and natural phenomena from a paper by Sendivogius in the *Bibliotheca Chemica Curiosa*

*Figura prima.*

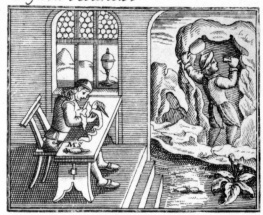

*Figura Secunda.*

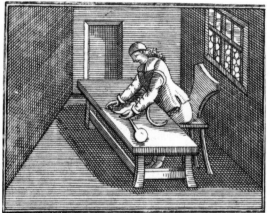

*Figura tertia.*

*Figura quarta.*

*Figura quinta.*

*Figura Pexta.*

MUTUS LIBER, IN QUO TAMEN tota Philoſophia herme-tica, figuris hieroglyphicis depingitur, ter optimo maximo Deo miſericordi conſecratus, ſolisque filiis artis dedicatus, authore cuius nomen eſt Altus.

2i. ii. 82. Neg:
93. 82. 72. Neg:
82. 81. 33. Tued.

Abraham's vision of the angels on the ladder: the mystic link between Heaven and Earth (from the *Liber Mutus*)

The alchemist and his *soror mystica* pray below the waters of the sky. Above, the angels support the vessel containing Neptune with Sol and Luna, beneath the Sun

*Opposite:* The first distillation offered to Luna; slow heating of the product

Preparation of the *materia prima* from cloths exposed in the fields to sun and rain

The created world: the *soror* fishes for Neptune and the *artifex* for Melusina in the inner depths

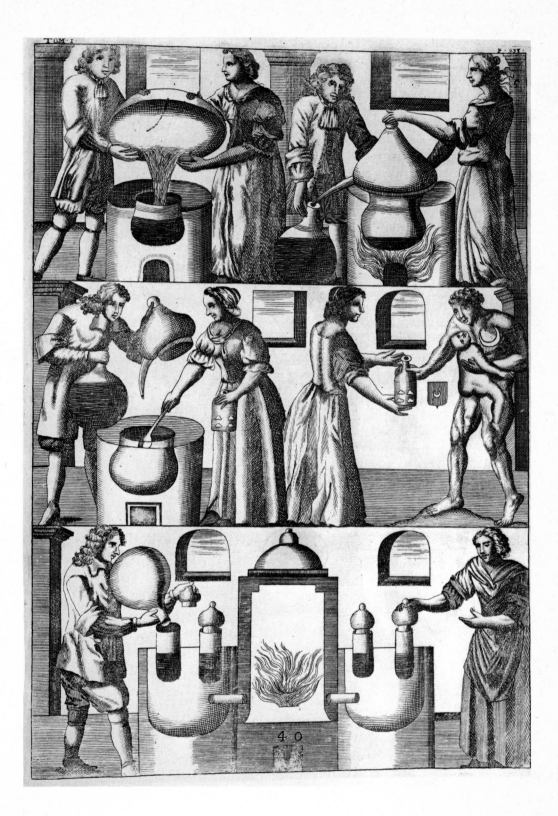

4. 0

Distillation and separation. Sol brings the Golden Flower. The crucible is prepared

Calcination and combination. The devouring Parent is burnt and revived by
Luna

*Opposite:* The distillate is exposed to nature, and is replaced by nature and Mercurius in the flasks

Weighing and mixing Sol and Mercury. The vessel is sealed and placed in the furnace. Sol and Luna unite

The angels bear Mercurius under the Sun. The *artifex* and *soror* prepare the vessel in the furnace

*Opposite:* Mercury is again in the alembic under the Sun. For the third time the *artifex* and *soror* pray beside their furnace

Weighing, mixing, placing in furnace. Here Sol and Luna unite in multiplication

The furnaces, opened for the 'assay of proof'. The secret, secretly known, is still secret

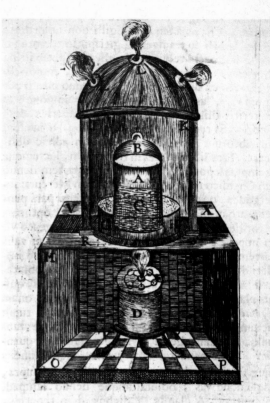

**EXPLICATIO FABRICÆ.**

A. *Vas vitreum materia C. refertum.*
B. *Operculum Vasi A. collutatum.*
G. H. *Tigillum arena refertum.*
D. *Lampas oleo olivarum referta.*
E. *Ellychnium subereis alis instructum.*
F. *Flamma lampadis.*
L L L *Spiracula subsequentis loculamenti.*
V X I K *Loculamentum intra quod vas A. vitreum collocatur.*
V X M N O P. *Abacus cui loculamentum superponitur ; in medio R S pertusum, ut flamma fundum vasis G H prope attingere queat.*
T Y *Tripes supra quem lampas ponatur.*
      *Tota fabrica deinde claudatur.*

Notice of a transformation performed before
Emperor Ferdinand III at Prague

The alchemist's furnace

*Opposite:* 'Given eyes to see, thou seest'. Mercurius, crowned by cupids, helps
the *artifex* and *soror* to rise, leaving the body and animal nature as dead, and
having no further use for the material ladder for their ascent

Medal struck from alchemical gold before His Serene Highness Charles Philip
Count Palatine of the Rhineland on 31 December 1716

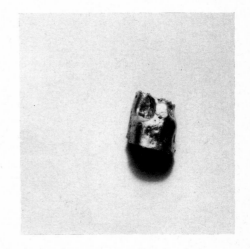

A specimen described as alchemical gold from the Department of Coins and
Medals, British Museum

pressures and temperatures more easily than the glass of ancient times. He had more exact methods of applying heat and could calculate it exactly in degrees centigrade instead of the ancient four degrees. At every stage he compares notes with the past, and after his description he quotes the *Golden Tractate of Hermes Trismegistus*, and Paracelsus's work *The Book of the Revelation of Hermes*. We can, therefore, see how closely he followed the ancient tradition.

Cockren tells us that, like so many other adepts, he worked at his experiments for forty years before he found the secret which would give real hope of success. Here is his account of what took place:

Here then, I entered upon a new course of experiment with a metal for experimental purposes of which I had no previous experience. This metal, after the long reduction to its essentials and undergoing separation and preparing a distillation deposit of the Mercury of the Philosophers, the Aqua Benedicta, the Aqua Celestes, and water of Paradise.

The first intimation I had of this triumph was a violent hissing, jets of vapour pouring from the retort and into the receiver like sharp bursts from a machine-gun, and then a violent explosion, whilst a very potent and subtle odour filled the laboratory and its surroundings. A friend has described this odour as resembling the dewy earth on a June morning, with the hint of growing flowers in the air; the breath of the wind over heather and hill, and the sweet smell of the rain on the parched earth.

Nicolas Flamel, after searching and experimenting from the age of twenty, wrote when he was eighty years old: 'Finally I found that which I desired, which I also soon knew by the strong scent and odour thereof.' Does this not coincide, this voice from the fourteenth century, with my discovery of the peculiar subtle odours? 'Cremer' also writes in the early fourteenth century: 'When this happy event takes place the whole house will be filled with a most wonderful sweet fragrance, and then will be the day of the nativity of this most blessed preparation'.

Having arrived at this point my next difficulty was to find a way of storing this subtle gas without danger to property. This I accomplished by coils of glass piping in water joined up with my receiver together with a perfect government of heat, the result being that the gas gradually condensed into a clear golden coloured water, very inflammable and very volatile. This water had then to be separated by distillation, the outcome being the white mercurial water described by the Comte de St Germain as his *athoeter*, or primary water of all the metals.

I will again quote from Manly Hall's introduction to *The Thrice Holy Trinosophie* the passage in which Casanova describes the *athoeter*: 'Then he showed me his magistrum which he called *Athoeter*. It was a white liquid contained in a white glass phial. He told me that the liquid was the Universal Spirit of Nature, and that if the wax on the stopper were pricked ever so slightly the whole of the contents would disappear. I begged him to make the experiment. He thereupon gave me the phial and the point and I myself pricked the wax, when lo, the phial was empty.' This passage aptly described the water, which is so volatile that it evaporates if left unstoppered, boils at a very low temperature, and does not so much as wet the fingers. This mercurial water, this *Athoeter* of St Germain, is absolutely necessary to obtain the oil of gold, which is obtained by its addition to the salts of gold after those salts have been washed by distilled water several times to remove the strong acidity of the *aqua regia* used to reduce the metal to that state. When the mercurial water is added to these salts of gold, there is a slight hissing, an increase of heat and the gold becomes a deep red liquid, from which is obtained by means of distillation the oil of gold, a deep amber liquid of an even consistency. This oil which is the potable gold of the Alchemist, never returns to the metallic form of gold. I can understand now, I think, how it is that some of the patients to whom salts of gold injections have been administered have succumbed to gold poisoning. So long as the salts are in an acid solution, they remain soluble, but directly the dissolving medium loses its acidity and becomes neutral or alkaline, the salts tend to form again into metallic gold. This is probably what happens in the case of the injection of gold salts into the intercellular fluids, which in some cases leads to fatal results.

Do not imagine that chemists know all about metals! They do not.

... From the golden water I have described can be obtained this white water, and a deep red tincture which deepens in colour the longer it is kept; these two are the Mercury and the Sulphur described by the Alchemists, Sol the Father and Lune the Mother, the Male and Female Principles, the White and Red Mercuries, which two, conjoined again form a deep amber liquid. This is the *Philosophic Gold*, which is *not* made from metallic gold but from another metal, and is a *far more potent* Elixir than the oil of gold. This deep amber liquid literally shines, and reflects and intensifies rays of light to an extraordinary degree. It has been described by many Alchemists, which fact again corroborates my work in the Laboratory. Indeed every step which I have taken in the laboratory I have found in the work of the various followers of the Spagiric Art.

... And now to the final goal, the Philosopher's Stone. Having found my two principles The Mercury and The Sulphur, my next step was to purify the dead body of the metal, that is the black dregs of the metal left after the extraction of the golden water. This was calcined to a redness and carefully separated and treated until it became a white salt. The three principles were then conjoined in certain exact quantities in a hermetically sealed flask in a fixed heat neither too hot nor too cold, care as to the exact degree of heat being essential, as any carelessness in its regulation would completely spoil the mixture.

On conjunction the mixture takes on the appearance of a leaden mud, which rises slowly like dough until it throws up a crystalline formation rather like a coral plant in growth. e 'flowThers' of this plant are composed of petals of crystal which are continually changing in colour. As the heat is raised the formation melts into an amber coloured liquid which gradually becomes thicker and thicker until it sinks into a black earth on the bottom of the glass. At this point (The sign of the Crow in Alchemical literature) more of the ferment or Mercury is added. In this process which is one of continued sublimation, a long necked, hermetically sealed flask is used, and one can watch the vapour rising up the neck of the flask and condensing down the sides. This process continues until the state of 'dry blackness' is attained. When more of the Mercury is added, the black powder is dissolved, and from this conjunction, it seems that a new substance is born, or, as the early Alchemists would have expressed it, a Son is born. As the black colour abates, colour after colour comes and goes until the mixture becomes white and shining; the White Elixir. The heat is gradually raised yet more and from white the colour changes to citrine and finally to red – the *Elixir Vitae*, the Philosopher's Stone, the medicine of Men and Metals. From their writings it appears that many alchemists found it unnecessary to take the Elixir to this very last stage, the citrine coloured solution being adequate for their purpose.

It is of interest to note that an entirely different manifestation comes into being after the separation of the three elements and their reconjunction under the sealed vase of Hermes. By the deliberate separation and unification of the Mercury, Sulphur and Salt, the three elements appear in a more perfect manifestation than in the first place.

This last account of a transmutation procedure is not different from the earlier accounts, except that a few more precise terms are added, and the outlook is much more pragmatic. But the careful concealment of the basic materials used and the use of the ancient similes leave us in the same quandary. Something is described not only by the alchemist but also by another witness and it does not agree with the expectations of scientific theory.

The contrast is practically complete. But it is one of the great concepts of alchemy that the essential unity is achieved through the amalgamation of opposites. There is a case for reserving judgement, not only based on the eccentric claims of alchemists, but on the realization of modern scientists that the basic structure of matter is indeterminate and occasionally unpredictable. It is clear that the few really reliable alchemical statements are concerned with a problem which is scientific. The main point of confusion is the curious unscientific language deliberately adopted by the alchemists, which confused them nearly as often as it confused other people. The medieval and classical ideas about the universe and the structure of matter were empirically true, but further research has made it clear that they were insufficiently described. In addition to the deliberate omissions and misdirections we have to cope with the change in scientific language which has developed with our increased knowledge of the universe.

When we look at the Cockren experiments we are presented with descriptions of recently observed phenomena, which clearly reproduce the alchemical experience. The interesting sharp sweet odours suggest that something is happening to produce ozone (the unstable molecule of three oxygen atoms) which is a temporary state of oxygen produced under conditions of extreme electrical tension. It is quite clear that the extremely volatile distillate and the coloured oily substances will mix; but what is surprising is that when separated and then mixed again a considerable change occurs. It is probably a matter of molecular rearrangement, rather like that which occurs when hard crystalline yellow sulphur is melted and boiled so that on cooling it congeals as a reddish material rather like a stiff jelly in consistency. Sulphur still has some real relationship to the alchemical process. The final experience given by Mr Cammell of the Cockren experiment, about the coral-like crystal of gold growing from a black *massa confusa* in the retort, is inexplicable according to our modern knowledge, but there are precedents in alchemical circles for such a happening. However, we are not told if Cockren ever continued his work to the point where a true red-powder, or golden hard wax-like Stone was produced, which was capable of material transmutation of a much greater weight of lead or mercury.

In the Helvetius story the coruscations of coloured light, which followed the addition of the mysterious Stone to the crucible of molten lead, again suggest some unknown electrical property. Have the alchemists made a solid ball-lightning? It is highly improbable. Considerable forces were evoked, however, and if no explosives like fulminate of mercury were involved there remains the possibility of steam explosions in the laboratory, of the kind which Cockren avoided by having good modern materials. But the manifestation which sounded like bursts of machine-gun fire to a man who had taken part in the First World War must have exhibited really considerable violence. Perhaps this was of the nature of a gas plasma?

As for the elixir, Cockren brings forward no new information, except that as a skilled medical man there is no doubt that he knew what he was talking about when he described the extreme volatility of one of the products. We owe the discovery of alcohol to the medieval alchemists, and many other substances, both acid and alkaline in nature. The alkahest may have been the volatile spirit, or even the strange odour which seemed to have penetrated the containers although they were hermetically sealed. The gold salts which Cockren alludes to were of professional interest to him, and do not fit in with the idea of a universal panacea. Maybe there was a quality in the personality of the expert alchemist which helped in a manner akin to faith healing. We have the example of Sir Kenelm Digby who, among many other brilliant accomplishments, earned a reputation as a healer by blessing bandages and treating them with an acid like vitriol, after which the patients who sent the bandages were healed at a distance. This is a phenomenon not usually associated with the alchemists, but there is no doubt that this band of good-hearted philosophers put the healing art high among the virtues of their Stone.

The mystery of alchemy is not only in the field of physical effects, but also of psychological development. It is clear that in the study of the alchemists we have to accept their double path as a unification of both physical and psychological concepts. As we know, the alchemical process reflected an intensified projection of the normal development of the human psyche. This must have produced a deep inner understanding of the whole process of human life, and of the inter-relationship of the person with the material universe. But such a development towards personal integration does not usually bring with it the power of working apparently material miracles. True the old alchemists never tired of comparing their work with the biblical statement that by faith one can move mountains. All the same we do not find modern counterparts of the alchemists in active public life. We are not aware of any gentle elderly philosopher healing by means of wondrous golden potions, or quietly producing bags of gold for his favourite charities. As things stand he would be sued by the medical bodies for the first, and prosecuted by the Treasury for the second. Even the mildest modern state must be an enemy of the alchemist, because they are mutually anachronistic. The alchemist is in need of a freedom of action and thought which has disappeared; the state is driven by the need to organize manpower for the well-being of the hugely enlarged human communities of today. The dilemma seems absolute. The answer is the old alchemical one of the reconciliation and union of opposites. How that can come about no one can say.

As we have seen there is good evidence that the alchemist has on rare occasions produced both useful medicines and beautiful gold. The twentieth century experience which we have described in the very words of Archibald Cockren is very much to the point. Cockren was able to use a modern laboratory and his own free time to follow a past procedure, which yielded positive results. The ancient ridiculous statements which could produce no reasonable result were tested. They produced a result but in an indescribable way. The reward earned by this long period of patient experiment, failure and re-experiment was only considerable from the point of view of a philosopher seeking to witness the unbelievable experience of the transmutation. In material terms this was an unprofitable venture. The cost of apparatus and power supply far outweighed the value of what was found.

The expenditure of half a lifetime in patient work did not earn a living wage.

The artist was a very true title for the alchemist. Only a long and devoted dedication to the mysterious path could lead him to the conclusion of his search. As in art the search has never been properly defined. It was a growth which brought personal enlightenment of the kind which all mystics seek, and with it came the possibility of the mysterious transmutation. There is no reason to suspect the alchemists of insanity. We must conclude that even a few well-checked examples of transmutation were sufficient to keep a small but devoted band of researchers busy with the fantastic search which absorbed all their energies. Cranks, they may have been, but that is not a dishonourable term.

The whole subject led to public curiosity and greed. This in turn nurtured a huge band of confidence tricksters and swindlers. Doubt was succeeded by dislike and even hatred. The alchemists were not only thought to be cheats or fools, but many were accused of dabbling in unlawful commerce with demons. After years of popularity the subject faded from attention, except among the small circles of occultists and people who wanted to find out what truth was behind a discredited superstition. As we have seen a little has emerged.

The testimony of Archibald Cockren suggests a strong element of doubt in our judgement of the alchemists. He shows that the accusations against them of lying and cheating remain 'not proven'. Only the future can give us a clear understanding of the whole matter.

# conclusion

There is no true conclusion to our subject. The mental attitudes which lead men to seek out hidden knowledge and to find satisfaction in personal revelations of divine approbation will continue as long as people remain. These are not evil things, but they are exclusive. As the alchemists wisely saw, all mankind is living at varying levels of development and the hidden knowledge of the secrets of nature must not be divulged to the mass of people. It is a knowledge for the humble and obscure philosopher, not for the brilliant leader of men or the adventurer seeking power over others.

The beginning are as old as the human knowledge of metals and their mysterious physical properties. Cockren's guess at a date of 1900 BC may not be far out. But since the earliest formulations of alchemical ideas there has been a linkage between the world of nature and the creative power of God. Alchemy grew and flourished in a world of social structures in which a philosophy of dialectical materialism was impossible. Mankind had not been faced by the horror of Britain and Germany in the industrial revolution, and the thought of a material power structure of the universe did not exist. Blake sounded something like the ancient religious voice of the true humanist when he denounced the 'dark satanic mills'. The alchemist also saw the materialistic search for power and profit as incompatible with the possession of knowledge of power beyond the dreams of the majority.

Life and creation was behind all the thought of alchemy from the earliest cults of earth and heaven. The world of matter was related to the world of men, and the beautiful wonder of human generation was seen to be like the relationship of created and Creator. The idea of alchemy must have been widespread in the Middle East long before the Roman Empire. That it first grew up in Egypt is natural, because of the ideal conditions of the climate and the annual fertilizing of the land during the Nile floods. But trade and religious contacts spread it abroad. The Greek philosophers found its parallel in the Mysteries. The Ptolemies gave Egypt the great university and *Museion* of Alexandria. There alchemy grew from technology to a form of religious worship. No doubt Maria the Jewess was one who taught in that great centre of civilized learning.

When the Arabs came into power, their philosophers soon learned to advance beyond their teachers. They were not so concerned with preserving the tradition of alchemy as advancing the scientific nature of the enquiry. In turn they taught the Europeans to speculate even more deeply on the mysteries of the material world. It was the fertilizing process of Arab and Catholic scholarship which wove alchemy into the fabric of religion in the dark ages, and developed it both in its scientific and philosophical aspects in medieval and early renaissance times.

The age of the Reformation and the following development of secular teaching did not destroy the ancient occult belief and strange practical devices of the alchemists. They achieved fame and retired from the dangers which accompanied it.

Then came the nadir of their hopes. They were unscientific, secretive, mysterious, and some worked within secret esoteric cultist societies. Gradually the whole subject was allowed to drift, with only a very few experimenters seeking out the ancient trail. In their darkest hour there was the literary search and exposition of Mary Anne Atwood, which must have stimulated several new approaches to the idea of alchemy. The official scientists were still barred from seeking beyond the limits of reason, but a few individuals worked on the problem. Probably the most successful in recent years has been Archibald Cockren. Much yet remains to be learnt about alchemy, not least about the development of human nature, which brings the spiritual gold of true individuation of the whole personality.

# ALCHEMICAL SYMBOLS

The Seven Planetary Metals

⊙ Gold    Sol

☽ Silver    Luna

♀ Copper    Venus

♂ Iron    Mars

☿ Mercury    Mercury

♄ Lead    Saturn

♃ Tin    Jupiter

The Twelve Processes in Zodiacal Time

♈ Aries    Calcination

♉ Taurus    Congelation

♊ Gemini    Fixation

♋ Cancer    Solution

♌ Leo    Digestion

♍ Virgo    Distillation

♎ Libra    Sublimation

♏ Scorpio    Separation

♐ Sagittarius    Ceration

♑ Capricornus    Fermentation

♒ Aquarius    Multiplication

♓ Pisces    Projection

Some other Symbols

▢ Common Salt

✳ Sal ammoniac

⊗ Salt fixed

♉ Realgar

☿ Sublimate of Mercury    [Example of combined signs    ☿♎ ]

The Four Elements

Air  △̶      △ Fire

Water  ▽      ▽̶ Earth

209

10—TAOTA

# BIBLIOGRApHY

There are seven important volumes of collected alchemical papers which contain most of our information on the subject. In the following short list the name of each volume is preceded by a letter in brackets; when this is found in the index of works it signifies that the work in question is to be found in the volume denoted by this reference letter.

(A)     *ARS CHEMICA, quod se licita recte exercentibus, probationes doctissimorum iurisconsultorum,* Strasbourg, 1566

(B)     *ARTIS AURIFERAE quam chemiam vocant,* Basel, 2 vols, 1593 (also 1572 and 1610 editions)

(C)     *BIBLIOTHECA CHEMICA CURIOSA, seu Rerum ad Alchemiam pertinentium thesaurus instructissimus* . . . 2 vols, Geneva, 1702

(D)     *DE ALCHEMIA: In hoc volumine de Alchemia continenta haec* . . . Nuremberg, 1541

(E)     *MUSAEUM HERMETICUM reformatum et amplificatum,* Frankfurt a/M, 1678 (and 2 vol translation by Waite), The Hermetic Museum

(F)     *THEATRUM CHEMICUM, praecipuos selectorum auctorum tractatus* . . . vols I, II, III, Ursel, 1602, vols IV, V, VI, Strasbourg, 1613, 1622, 1661

(G)     *THEATRUM CHEMICUM BRITANNICUM:* collected with annotations by Elias Ashmole, London, 1652

Abu 'l-Qasim Muhammad ibn Ahmad al-Iraqui: *Book of Knowledge acquired concerning the cultivation of Gold,* (trans. E. J. Holmyard) Paris, 1923

Aegidius de Vadis: *Dialogus inter Naturam et filium philosophiae* (F)

Agrippa von Nettesheim, Cornelius: *The Vanity of Arts and Sciences,* London, 1676

Albertus Magnus, Saint: *Liber octo capitulorum de lapide philosophorum* (F)

——*Scriptum super arborem Aristotelis* (F)

'Ali, M. Turab (editor): *Three Arabic Treatises on Alchemy by Muhammad bin Umail.* Memoirs of the Asiatic Society of Bengal. XII. Calcutta, 1933

*Allegoria Merlini* (B)

*Allegoriae sapientum supra librum Turbae XXIX distinctiones,* (F)

*Allegoriae super librum Turbae* (B)

Altus (pseudonym): *Mutus Liber,* La Rochelle, 1677, also in (C)

*Ambix,* London, Edited F. Sherwood Taylor, 1937 . . .

Antonie, Francis: *Aurum Potabile; or the receipt of Fr. Antonie,* London, 1893 and 1963

*Aphorisme Basiliani sive Canones Hermetici* (F)

*Aquarium sapientum* (E)

*Arcanum Hermeticae philosophiae opus*, Geneva, 1653

Arisleus: *Visio Arislei* (B)

Aristotle (pseudonym): *Tractatus Aristotleis Alchymistae ad Alexandrum Magnum, de Lapide philosophico* (B) and (F)

Arnaldus de Villa Nova: *Speculum Alchimiae* (F)

—— *Thesaurus Thesaurum* (B)

—— *Rosarius* (B)

Artefius: *Clavis maioris sapientiae* (C) and (F)

Atwood, Mary Anne: *A Suggestive Enquiry into the Hermetic Mystery*, revised edn, Belfast, 1920; New York, 1960

*Aurelia occultum philosophorum* (F)

*Aurum Vellus* (F)

*Aurora consurgens* (B)

*Authoris ignoti, philosophici lapidis secreta metaphorici describensis* (B)

Avicenna: *Tractatulus Avicennae* (B)

Bacxstrom, Sigismund: *Alchemical Anthology*, London, 1960

Bernard of Treviso: *Liber de alchemia: De chemico miraculo quod lapidem philosophiae appelant* (F)

Berthelot, Marcellin: *La Chimie au moyen âge*, 3 vols, Paris, 1893

—— *Collection des anciens alchimistes grecs*, Paris, 1885

—— *Les Origines de l'Alchimie*, Paris, 1885

Boehme, Jakob: *The Works of Jacob Behmen*, 4 vols, London, 1764–81

Bonus, Petrus: *Pretiosa margarits novella* (C) and (F)

Bouche-Leclercq, Auguste: *L'Astrologie grecque*, Paris, 1899

Budge, E. A. Wallis: *The Gods of the Egyptians*, 2 vols, London, 1904

Cammell, Charles R.: *Heart of Scotland*, London, 1956

Christopher of Paris: *Elucidarius artis transmutatoriae metallorum summa major* (G)

Cockren, Archibald: *Alchemy Rediscovered and Restored*, London, 1956

*Codices* and MSS:

Berlin: *Cod. Berolinus Latinus* 532, fol. 147–164

Florence, Bibliotheca Medicea-Laurenziana: Ashburnham MS 1166; *Miscellanea de alchimia*, fourteenth century

Oxford, Bodleian Library: MS Ashmole, 1394, Ripley: *Cantilena*, seventeenth century

—— MS Ashmole 1445, Ripley: *Cantilena*

—— MS Bruce 96 (*Codex Brucianus*) *A Coptic Gnostic Treatise*

Paris, Bibliothèque Nationale: MS 2327, *Livre sur l'Art de faire l'or*, 1478

—— MS Français 14765, *Abraham le Juif: Livre des figures Hieroglyphiques*

St Gallen: *Codex Germanicus Alchemicus Vadiensis*, sixteenth century

*Consilium Conjugii*: (A), (C) and (F)

Curtius, Ernest Robert: *European Literature and the Later Middle Ages*, New York, Bollingen Series XXXVI, and London, 1953

Dee, John: *Monas Hieroglyphica* (F)

Delphinas: *Liber secreti maximi* (F)

# Bibliography

*De magni lapidis compositione et operatione* (F)

D'Espagnet: *Arcanum Hermeticae philosophiae opus* (C)

Dorn, Gerhard: Nine works included in (F)

—— *Theophrasti Paracelsi Libri V de Vita longa*, Frankfurt a/M, 1583

Eisler, Robert: *Zur Terminologie und Geschichte der jüdischen Alchemie* (*Monatschrift f. Geschichte u. Wissenschaft der Judentums*), Dresden, vol LXX, pp. 194–201, 1926

*Epistola ad Hermannum archiepiscopum Coloniensem de lapide philosophorum* (F)

Flamel, Nicolas: *Nicolas Flamel, his explanation of the hieroglyphicall figures etc*, by Eirenaeus Orandus, London, 1624

—— *Summarium philosophicum* (E)

Franz, Marie-Louise von: *Aurora consurgens; A document of the Alchemical Problem of Opposites, Attributed to Thomas Aquinas*, New York (Bollingen Series) and London, 1963

Geber (Jabir): *Summa perfectionis* (D)

——*Works*, London, 1678; ed. E. J. Holmyard, London, 1928

Goethe, Johann, Wolfgang von: *Faust*, English translation, 2 vols Harmondsworth, 1949 and 1959

Grasseus, Johannes: *Arca Arcani* (F)

Gratarolus, Guilielmus: *Verae alchemiae artisque metallicae, citra enigmata*, Basel, 1561 and (B)

Greverus, Jodocus: *Secretum* (F)

Hastings, James: *Encyclopaedia of Religion and Ethics*, 13 vols, Edinburgh and New York, 1908–27

Helvetius, Johann Friedrich: *Vitulus aureus* (E)

Hermas: *The Shepherd* in *The Apostolic Fathers*, vol II (Loeb Classical Library), London and New York, 1913

Hermes Trismegistus: *Tractatus aureus* (C) and (A)

Hoffman, Ernst Th. William: *The Devil's Elixir*, 2 vols, Edinburgh, 1824

Hoghelande, Theobald de: *De alchemiae difficultatibus* (C) and (F)

Hollandus, Johannes Isaacus: *Fragmentum de opere philosophorum* and *Operum mineralium liber* (F)

Holmyard, Eric J. (trans): *Abu l'Qasim al Iraqui* (Geber) in *Isis*, Wandelgem-le-Gand, 1926

—— *Alchemy*, Harmondsworth, 1953

Hopkins, A. J.: *Alchemy, Child of Greek Philosophy*, London, 1930

Horapollo Niliacus: *The Hieroglyphics*, Bollingen Series XXIII, New York, 1950

*Isis*: ed. George Sarton, Wandelgem-le-Gand . . .

*Jewish Encyclopaedia, The*: Ed. I. Singer, 12 vols, New York and London, 1925

Johnson, O. S.: *A Study of Chinese Alchemy*, London, 1928

Jung, Carl Gustav: *Psychology and Alchemy* in *Collected Works*, vol 12, London, 1953

—— *Mysterium Conjunctionis*, in *Collected Works*, vol 14, London, 1963

Khalid: *Liber Secretorum*, and *Liber trium verborum* (B)

Khunrath, Heinrich: *Amphitheatrum sapientiae*, Hanau, 1609

Lambspringk: *De lapide philosophico figurae at emblemata* (E)

Larguier, Leo: *Le Faiseur d'or Nicolas Flamel*, Paris, 1936

Lenglet du Fresnoy, Pierre Nicolas: *Histoire de la philosophie Hermetique*, Paris and The Hague, 3 vols, 1742

Li Shi Chang: *Travels of an Alchemist*, ed. Arthur Waley, London, 1931 and 1963

*Liber de arte chymica* (B)

*Liber de magni lapidis compositione* (F)

Madathanus, Henricus: *Aureum saeculum redivivum* (E)

Maier, Michael: *Atalanta fugiens, hoc est, emblemata nova de secretis naturae chymica,* Oppenheim, 1618

—— *Secretioris naturae secretorum scrutinium chymicum,* Frankfurt a/M, 1687

—— *Symbola aureae mensae duodecim nationum,* Frankfurt a/M, 1617

Malvasius, Caesar: *Aelia Laelia Crispis non nata resurgens,* Bologna, 1683

Maria Prophetissa: *Practica in artem alchimicam* (B)

Mead, George Robert Stow (ed. and trans.) *Thrice Greatest Hermes,* 3 vols, London 1949

Meung, Jean de: *Demonstratio naturae* (E)

Mennens, William: *Aurei velleris sive sacrae philosophiae vatum selectae et unicae Libri tres* (F)

Merlinus: *Allegoria de arcano lapidis* (B)

Micreris: *Tractatus Micreris suo discipulo Mirnefindo* (F)

Morienus Romanus: *De transmutatione metallica* (B)

Mutus Liber: *see* Altus

Mylius, Johann Daniel: *Philosophia reformata,* Frankfurt a/M, 1622

Norton, Thomas: *The Ordinall of Alchemy* (G)

*Occult Observer, The,* London, 1949–50

Paracelsus (Theophrastus Bombastus von Hohenheim): *Aureoli Philippi Theophrasti Bombasts von Hohenheim Paracelsi: Philosophi und Medici Opera Bücher und Schriften,* 10 parts, Strasbourg, 1589–90

Penotus: *Caracteres secretorum celandorum* (F)

—— *De medicamentis chemicis* (F)

—— *Quinquagintaseptem canones de opere physico* (F)

Petrus de Silento: *Opera* (F)

Philalethes, Eirenaeus: *Introitus apertus ad occlusum regis palatium* and *Fons chymicae veritatis* (E)

—— *Preparation of the Sophic Mercury,* London, 1893, 1963

Read, John: *Prelude to Chemistry,* London, 1939

Ripley, Sir George: *Omnia opera chemica,* London, 1649

—— *Duodecimum portarium axiomata philosophica* (F)

—— *The Bosom Book of Sir George Ripley,* London, 1893, 1963

*Rosarium philosophorum* (B)

Rosencreutz, Christian (= Johann Valentin Andreae): *Hermetick Romance or the Chymical Wedding,* trans E. Foxcroft, London, 1690

*Rosinus ad Euthiciam* (B)

*Rosinus ad Sarratantam Episcopum* (B)

Roth-Scholtz, Friedrich: *Deutsches Theatrum Chemicum,* 3 vols, Nuremberg, 1728–1732

Ruland, Martin: *A Lexicon of Alchemy,* London, 1892 (trans. of Frankfurt Latin edition of 1622)

Ruska, Julius: *Die vision des Arisleus,* 'Georg Sticker Festschrift', Berlin, 1930

—— *Studien zu Muhammad ibn Umail,* in *Isis* XXIV, Bruges, 1935–1936

—— *Tabula Smaragdina,* Heidelberg, 1926

—— *Turba Philosophorum,* Berlin, 1931

Ruysbroeck, John of: *Scala Philosophorum* (B)

Scott, Walter: *Hermetica,* 4 vols, Oxford, 1924–36

# Bibliography

Sendivogius, Michael: *Parabola, seu Aenigma Philosophicum . . . Novum lumen chemicum,* and *Tractatus de Sulphure* (F)

Senior: *De chemia Senioris antiquissimi philosophi libellus* (C) and (F)

Singer, Mrs Charles (Dorothea Waley): *Catalogue of Western Alchemical Manuscripts,* 3 vols, Union Académique Internationale, 1928–31

Starkey, George: *The Oil of Sulphur,* London, 1665, 1893, 1963

——*The Stone of the Philosophers,* undated (seventeenth century), London, 1893

Steinerus, Henricus: *Dissertatio chymico-medica inauguralis de Antimonio,* Basel, 1699

Stolcius de Stolcenberg, Daniel: *Viridarium Chymicum,* Frankfurt a/M, 1624

Taylor, F. Sherwood: *The Alchemists,* London, 1951

Tetzen, Johannes de (Johannes Ticinensis): *Processus de Lapide Philosophorum,* Hamburg, 1670

Thorndike, Lynn: *A History of Magic and Experimental Science,* 8 vols, New York, 1923–1958

Trismosin, Salomon; *Aureum vellus, oder Guldin Schatz und Kunstkammer,* Rorschach, 1598 (this includes *Splendor Solis* as the *Tractatus Tertius*)

—— (English edition *Splendor Solis: Alchemical treatises,* edited by G.K., London, 1920)

*Turba Philosophorum* (B)

Valentinus, Basilius: *Chymische schriften,* Hamburg, 1677

—— *De prima materia lapidis philosophici* (E)

—— *Opus praeclarum ad utrumque* (F)

—— *The Triumphal Chariot of Antimony,* ed. A. Waite, London, 1893 and 1962

Vaughan, Thomas: *The Works of Thomas Vaughan; Eugenius Philaletha,* ed. A. E. Waite, London, 1919

Waite, Arthur Edward: *The Holy Kabbalah,* London, 1929

—— *The Real History of the Rosicrucians,* London, 1887

—— (ed. and trans.) *The Hermetic Museum, Restored and Enlarged,* 2 vols, London, 1893 and 1953

Waley, Arthur: (trans) *The Way and Its Power,* London, 1934

White, Richard, of Basingstoke: *Aelia Laelia Crispis Epitaphium,* Dordrecht, 1618

Wilhelm, Richard: *The Secret of the Golden Flower,* with commentary by C. G. Jung, London and New York, 1931 and 1962

Zacharias, Dionysius: *Opusculum philosophiae naturalis metallorum, cum annotationibus Nicolai Flamelli* (F)

# index

Abbasid dynasty, 29
Abelard, 41
Abu Ali ibn Sina, *see* Avicenna
acids, 23, 31, 141
Adam, 159
Aesir, 21
Aetius, 20
Agatho Priscus, Lucius, 158
agrimony, 67
air, element, 8, 23
Albertus Magnus, 41, 42, 171–2
albification, 67
Albigenses, 18, 42
*Alchemists, The* (Taylor), 24
*Alchemy Rediscovered and Restored* (Cockren), 184
alcohol, 70, 141, 204
alembic, 31, 140
Alexander the Great, 67
Alexandria, 2, 4, 7–8, 17, 22, 26, 48, 208
alkahest, 204
alkali, 67
allegory, alchemy as, 95
 – of nature, 23, 39
alloys, 4–5, 23
alum, 67
altar, symbolism of, 23, 25
American Indians, 5, 97
*Amphitheatrum Sapientiae* (Khunrath), 93
Anabaptists, 94
angel, vision of, 48, 74
*anima*, 79, 118, 141
antimony, 179
apparatus of alchemist, 22, 67
apports, 48, 101
Apuleius, Lucius, 17
Apulia, 39, 41

*Aqua Benedicta*, 201
*Aqua Celestis*, 201
*Aqua Fortis*, 77, 169, 184
*Aqua Regia* (*Regis*), 183–4, 202
Arabs, 2, 26, 28, 68, 122, 208 *see also* Islam
archetypal dreams, 18, 48
 – myths, 37, 71, 120
 – symbols, 140
Arianism, 21, 26
Aristotle, 8, 17, 19, 21
 pseudo-Aristotle, 67
Arnold of Villanova, 42–4
arsenic, 67
Artorius, 20
Asar-Hap, *see* Serapis
Ashmole, Elias, 172, 179–80
astral light, 184
astrology, 6, 94
*athoeter*, 201–2
atomic theory, 8, 38, 41
Attila, 20
Atwood, Mrs A. T., 127–8, 137, 208
Avicenna, 33–4, 41
Avignon, 75

Babylon, 6, 153
Backhouse, William, 179
Bacon, Roger, 42–4
Baldur, 37
Banks, Sir Joseph, 118, 181
Barmecide family, 30
Barnes, 91
Belisarius, 20
Berlin, 116
'blackness of black', 177
Blake, William, 122, 124, 207
Boehme, Jakob, 2, 99, 122

Bokhara, 33
Bologna, 158
*Book of Abraham the Jew*, 48, 65
*Book of the Composition of Alchemy*, 41
*Book of the Revelation of Hermes* (Paracelsus), 201
*Book of Venus* (Jabir), 30
book, vision of, 48, 65
borax, 97, 117
*Bosom Book* (Ripley), 179
Boyle, Robert, 98
brass, 45
Bridlington, 76
brimstone, 67 *see also* sulphur
Bristol, 80
British Museum, 181
*Brotherhood of the Rosy Cross* (Waite), 180
Brussels, 116
Bungay, Friar, 44
Byzantium, 20, 21, 26-7, 30, 40, 69, 160

*caelum*, 172
Caetano, Manuel, 116
Cagliostro, Alessandro di, 115, 121
Cammell, C. R., 183, 204
*Canon's Yeoman's Tale* (Chaucer), 66-8
cartomancy, 121
Casanova de Seingalt, G. J., 201-2
Catholicism, 21
Caucasus, 5
*Cauda Pavonis, see* Peacock's Tail
Celtic mythology, 18, 21, 25, 37
Ch'ang-Chun, 159
chariot, symbolism of, 160, 169
charlatanry, 45, 66, 99, 115, 206
Charlemagne, 30, 33, 37
Charles XII of Sweden, 116
Charnock, Thomas, 89
Chaucer, Geoffrey, 1, 66-8
chemistry, 18, 41, 68, 90, 137
China, 18, 21, 159
Christ, life of, parallel found with, 44
Christian II, Elector of Saxony, 95
Christian liturgy, 71, 77
Chronos (time), identified with Cronos, 142
cinnabar, 6
citrination, 68
classical studies, 121
classification of materials, 31, 32
clay, 67
Cleopatra, 25
clock, invention of, 33

Cockren, Archibald, 183-4, 201-6, 207, 208
Colombia, 5
colouring of metals, superficial, 24, 34, 41
colours, change of, 72, 77, 177, 203
commerce, 69
Commune, Paris, 126
Communist Manifesto, 126
Constantine the Great, 21
copper, 5-6, 25, 68
    transmuted to gold, 45, 92
    to gold and silver, 106
Coptic Church, 21, 26
Cordoba, 33, 40, 69
corpse, symbolism of, 71
Corsica, 40
Counter-Reformation, 78
Cracow, 91
creation, theories of, 6-7, 21, 140, 144
'Cremer, Abbot', 45, 201
crosslet, 67
crow, head of, 177
    sign of, 203
Crusades, 38, 40
cucurbite, 67
Cyprus, 5

Damascus, 28, 144
Dashwood, Sir Francis, 121
Dastyn, John, 75
*De lapide philosophorum* (Albertus Magnus), 171
Dee, Dr Arthur, 98
Dee, Dr John, 91
descensory, 67
Digby, Sir Kenelm, 97, 98-9, 101, 204
dimensions, 2, 3, 25, 172
Diocletian, 184
Dionysian cults, 140
Dioscorides, 23
distillation, 22, 31, 71-2, 201-2
*Divine Poimandres*, 156
Dorn, Gerhard, 172-3
dragons, Northern mythology, 18, 21, 37
    green, 71, 77, 141
    red, 76
Druids, 37
dung, *see* ordure

*Early Magnetism in its Higher Relations* (Atwood), 127
earth, element, 3, 8, 23, 156
    as mother, 141

earth—*continued*
  as nurse, 2
  — and heaven, 3, 141
Edward III, 45
egg, distillation of, 24
  white of, 67
Egypt, 2, 4, 7, 21, 26, 40, 70, 116, 118, 120, 121,
    153, 184, 207
Eirenaeus, 169
electricity, 74, 75, 184, 203
elements, four, 3, 8, 21, 23, 31, 70, 98, 141, 159,
    160, 171, 179
Eleusis, 7, 25, 155
'Elias', 101
elixir, 31, 32, 176
  derivation, 157
  transmutant and medicine, 101, 154, 172, 177,
    179, 203
  — of life (vitae), 37, 90, 203
  red, 47, 65
  white, 47, 65, 72, 203
  yellow, 101
  extracted from gold, 75
  *see also* Philosopher's Stone, powder, tincture
Elizabeth I, 89, 91, 92
embryo, development of, 25
*Emerald Tablet*, see *Tabula Smaragdina*
ether, 184
Etruscans, 158
excrement, *see* ordure
*Experience and Philosophy*, 172

Far East, 18
father, symbolism of, 2, 173
Faust, 79, 125
fermentation, 67, 70, 157
fire, element, 3, 8, 23, 98, 141
fire-serpents, 18
fires of rebirth, 18
  mystic —, 21
Flamel, Nicolas, 47–8, 65, 68, 143, 178, 182,
    184, 201
Flamel, Pernelle, 48
flowers of the Stone, 47, 203
fluids, weightless, 75, 123, 144
forgetting of secret, 89
France, 18, 21, 24, 34
Franciscan Order, 43
*Frankenstein* (Mary Shelley), 125
Franks, 20, 27
Freiherr, 122, 124

French Revolution, 121
Freud, Sigmund, 137–8

Garden of Paradise, 142
Geb, 120
Geber, *see* Jabir ibn Hayyan
gems, 102, 176
Gerbert of Aurillac (Pope Sylvester II), 33
'gibberish', derivation, 30
gilding, 6, 8, 23
Glastonbury, 92
gnomon, 31
Gnosticism, 21, 26, 79
Goethe, J. W. von, 125
gold, 5, 142, 157, 176
  as masculine, 176
  as king of metals, 5
  as purified soul, 19
  as sun, 5, 73, 157
  transmuted from brass and copper, 45
    from copper, 92, 106
    from lead, 95, 103, 113
    from mercury, 44, 65, 70, 72, 90, 97, 118
*Gold Making of Cleopatra*, 24
*Golden Ass* (Apuleius), 17
*Golden Tractate* 156–8, 201
goldsmiths, 17
Gosport, 127, 128
Goths, 20
Greek atomists, 8
Greek numerology, 30
guilds, 17
gunpowder, 46

Hague, The, 100
Hall, Manly, 201
Han dynasty, 18
Hāpi, 70
Hapsburg dynasty, 93
Haroun er Rashid, 30
Hathor, 153
*Heart of Scotland* (Cammell), 183
heavens, three, 38–9
Hellenistic texts, 4
Helvetius (Schweitzer), J. F., 100–4, 113–4,
    143, 179
herbs, 67, 70
hermaphrodite, 79
Hermes, 113, 203
  identified with Mercury, 6
  with Thoth, 7

Hermes—*continued*
  texts ascribed to, 67, 68
Hermes Trismegistus, 184
  translation of title of Thoth, 2, 7, 116
  texts ascribed to, 2–3, 7, 22, 156, 201
*hieros gamos*, 119
Hilarion, Benedict, 180
Holmyard, E. J., 6, 47
Holway, William, 89
Holy Grail, 37
horn-like material, 74
humours, four, 17
Huns, 20
*Hunting the Greene Lyon* (Eirenaeus), 169
Hunyades, Johannes, 98
hydrochloric acid, 141

illumination of manuscripts, 47
Incarnation, 170
India, 7
Indies, 78
individuation (Jung), 25, 73, 122, 155
industrial revolution, 124, 207
inner nature of metals, 32
Iraq, 28, 40
iridescence, 24, 37 *see also* Peacock's Tail
iron, 5–6, 68
Iron Age, 5
Isis, 17
Islam, 26–7, 28, 36, 38, 116, 126, 144
Isma' ili sect, 28, 31, 154
ixir, 157–8 *see also* elixir

Jabir ibn Hayyan, 29–33
jade, 159
Ja'far al Sadiq, 30
Ja'far the Barmecide, 30
Jerusalem, 40
Jews, 7, 126
John XXII, Pope, 75
Jonson, Ben, 1
Jung, C. G., 24, 25, 38, 73, 75, 79, 122, 128, 138, 139, 155, 160, 175
Jupiter, 68

*Kabbalah*, 6, 65, 126
Kelly, Edward, 91
Keridwen, Cauldron of, 25, 37
*kerotakis*, 23, 31, 37, 70, 140
Khalid, Prince, 28–9, 34, 160
Khunrath, Heinrich, 93, 99, 121, 122, 175, 180

king, symbolism of, 5, 76, 119
Knights Templars, 42, 44
Kufa, 29, 30

Laelia Crispis, Aelia, 158
Laski, Count Albert, 91
Latin, 41
lead, 68, 178
  found in nature with silver, 5
  transmuted to silver, 70, 72
    to gold, 74, 95, 103, 113
Leiden papyrus, 24
letters, symbolism of, 29–30, 31–2
lime, 67
lion, green, 76, 169
  white and red, 71
Louvain, 75
*Lucerna Salis* (Digby), 98
Lully, Raymond, 44, 45–6
Luna, *see* moon

Mabinogion, 37
Magdeburg, 93
Maghrib, 40
magic, 90, 121
magic square, 31
Maier, Michael, 179–80
Manichaeism, 18, 21, 26, 27, 28, 40, 76, 79, 153, 159
manikin, 25
Maria Prophetissa, 2, 22–3, 24, 70, 208
Maria the Jewess, *see* Maria Prophetissa
Marianus, *see* Morienus
*Marrow of Alchemy* (Eirenaeus), 169
Mars, 5–6, 68, 170
Marsh of Creation, 153
Maslama ibn Ahmad, 33
Masonic cults, 153
*massa confusa*, 7, 204
*materia prima*, 73, 77, 79, 122, 125, 141, 142, 160, 179, 180
materials of alchemist, 67–8, 70, 116, 117, 142
medals, gold, 115, 116, 181
medicine, 31, 89–90, 97, 205 *see also* elixir
Medmenham, 121
Melchior Cibinensis, 169
Melusina, 141, 142
Memphis, 121
menstruum, 104
mercurial water, 170, 201
Mercury (Mercurius), planet and god

Mercury (Mercurius)–*continued*
  identified with Hermes, 6
  as hermaphrodite, 79, 142
  symbol of, 101
  *see also* mercury, metal
mercury (quicksilver), metal, discovered, 6
  distillation, 23
  fulminate of, 44
  constituent of all metals, 34, 43, 176, 180
  associated with planet, 6, 68, 141, 170–1
  as feminine, 176
  as soul, 180
  symbolized as grey wolf, 77
  actuated –, 177
  philosophical –, 171–2, 176, 201, 202–3
  transmuted to silver, 90, 117–8
    to gold, 44, 65, 70, 72, 90, 97, 118
mercury poisoning, 67
Meridian of the Sun, 25
Mesmerism, 121, 128, 137
Mesopotamia, 5
metallurgy, 18
metals, associated with planets, 5–6, 39, 68
  deposition of, 23
  constitution of, 32, 34, 43, 144, 176, 180
Mexico, 74
microcosm and macrocosm, 39, 123
milk, 70
Miriam, 2, 22 *see also* Maria Prophetissa
Monophysites, 27
moon (Luna), 2, 24, 68, 141, 156, 170
  in Celtic mythology, 37
  associated with silver, 5, 73
  as feminine, 79, 141
  shadow of sun, 172
  symbol of, 102
moonwort, 67
Morienus, 28–9, 34, 160
Mormonism, 126
Morocco, 34
Moses, 2
mother, symbolism of, 2, 173
Muawiya II, Caliph, 28
Muhammad ibn Umail, 33
*Museion, see* Alexandria
mystery religions, 119, 207
mythology, Christian, of alchemists, 79–80

Napoleon, 116, 121
Narcissus, 113
Natural Sulphur, 170

Neoplatonism, 29
Nergal, 5
Nestorians, 27, 28
Newton, Sir Isaac, 2, 99, 120
Nibelungs, 20
Nifelheim, 37, 142
*nigredo*, 71, 171
Nile, 7, 70, 118, 153
nitre, 117
nitric acid, 31
Normans, 39–40
Norse mythology, 18, 21, 37
Norton, Thomas, 80, 89, 173–5
numerology, 29–30, 43
Nut, 120

occultism, 121, 125
Odin, 37
odour, 201, 204
*Of the Nature of Things* (Paracelsus), 183–4
oil of gold, 202
opposites, 2–3, 24, 39, 42, 73, 155–6
  above and below, 2–3, 156, 159, 184
  bright and dark, 2–3, 37, 76
*Ordinall of Alchemy* (Norton), 80, 173–5
ordure, 67, 70, 153, 157
Orphism, 153
orpiment (yellow arsenic), 68
Ouroboros, 24, 25
outer nature of metals, 32
Oxford, 43
oxydization, 24
ozone, 204

Palmerston, Lord, 117, 118
Pamplona, 41
Panacea, 178, 179 *see also* elixir
Paracelsus (Theophrastus Bombastus), 89–90,
    125, 183–4, 201
Paris, 43
Paykhull, General, 116
Peacock's Tail, 24, 44, 72, 177
Perfected Sulphur, 24
perfection, *see* purification
Persia, 7, 28
personality of alchemist, 39, 46, 78–9, 117, 142
    *see also* purification
Peru, 5, 74
Philippe le Bel, 42
philosopher, vision of, 74
Philosopher's Stone, 46–7, 70, 203

Philosopher's Stone—*continued*
  and gilding, 6
  flowers of the Stone, 47
  Natural Sulphur, 170
  ineffable substance, 46
  panacea, 178
  *see also* powder, elixir
philosophic gold, 32, 142, 202
Philosophic Water, 72
Phoenix, 72, 76, 141
pictorial expression, 36–7
planets, associated with metals, 5–6, 39, 68, 141
  symbols of, 17
  conjunction of, 70
platinum, 5, 97
Plato, 38
poetic symbolism, 7, 76
Poland, 91
polarity, *see* opposites
Polynesian mythology, 119, 120
potable gold, 202
powder, red, 32, 44, 46, 72, 92, 118, 178
  fulminate of mercury, 44
  mysterious origin of, 90, 92, 118
  *see also* elixir, Philosopher's Stone
powder, white, elixir, 32, 117
  intermediate stage, 117, 141
Prague, 91–3, 95
*prana*, 184
prayer, 71
Price, James, 117–8, 181
priest, symbolism of, 23, 25
primal material, *see materia prima*
prophet, symbolism of, 25
psychedelic art, 154
psychoanalysis, 137–8
*Psychology and Alchemy* (Jung), 38
Ptolemies, 4, 8, 207
Ptolemy II Philadelphus, 8
'puffers', 3, 17, 69, 73, 100, 117
purification, of metals, 5, 43
  associated with purification of soul, 7, 18, 23, 44
  of nature, 46, 70
putrefaction, 70, 177

qualities, four, 8, 17, 31
queen, symbolism of, 5, 76, 119
quicksilver, *see* mercury
quintessence, 184

rainbow, *see* Peacock's Tail
Razi, Al, 34
realgar (red arsenic), 68
Reason, Age of, 120–1
reflux apparatus, 22
Reformation, 78
Rembrandt, 1
Renaissance, 2, 119
repetition of process, 72, 124
*Rerum Novarum* (encyclical), 126
Rhodes, 75
Ripley, George, 75–7, 179
*Ripley Scrowles*, 76
Robert of Chester, 41
Romantic Movement, 124–5
Rome, 2, 17, 75
'Rosary of the Philosophers', 43
rose, mystic, 42
Rosicrucians, 144, 179–80
Royal Licences, 66
Royal Society, 118
rubifying water, 67
Rudolf II, 91–3, 95–7

St Bernard, 41
St Dunstan, 92
St Francis of Assisi, 144
St Germain, Comte de, 91, 115, 121, 184, 201–2
St-Jacques-la-Boucherie, 48, 65
St John of Jerusalem, Order of, 76
St Mary Redcliffe, Bristol, 80
St Paul, 144
St Thomas Aquinas, 41, 42
sal ammoniac, 67, 68
sal tartare, 67
Salisbury, 89
salt, 67, 104, 176, 180, 203
saltpetre, 67
Salvation Army, 126
*Salve Regina*, 170
Saracens, 26
Saturn, 68
*Sceptical Chymist* (Boyle), 98
Schweitzer, J. F., *see* Helvetius
science, experimental, 23, 41, 68, 90, 137
secret doctrines, 7, 21–2, 173–5
*Secreta Secretorum*, 67
Seljuk Turks, 40
semen, 70
Semitic thought, 6
Sendivogius, Michael, 95

# Index

Serapis, 7, 17

Sericum, 157

serpent, 24, 25, 160, 169, 171

Serpent's Egg, 37

Sesostris II, 184

Seton, Alexander, 95

sexual symbolism, 19, 23, 42, 79, 119–20, 153, 170–1

Shiism, 40

ship, symbolism of, 141

Sicily, 40

silver, 5, 65, 68, 72, 118, 177
   as moon, 5, 73
   transmuted from copper, 106
      from lead, 70, 72
      from mercury, 117–8

Sylvester II, Pope, *see* Gerbert of Aurillac

smelting, 4, 5

Sol, *see* sun

*Song of Solomon*, 71

*Soror Mystica*, 42, 91, 118

soul, 23, 28, 98, 159 *see also* purification

South, Mary Anne, *see* Atwood

South, Thomas, 127, 128

spagiric art, 2, 100, 144, 172

Spain, 20, 33, 40, 116

Sperm of the Philosophers, 170

spirits, 68

Spiritualism, 126, 128, 137

spontaneous generation, 7, 120

Starkey, George, 176–9

stars, 24

still, 22, 31, 140

Stockholm, 116

Stoke d'Abernon, 117

*Stone of the Philosophers* (Starkey), 176–9

Stonehenge, 184

stranger, vision of, 74, 101, 143

Sturlasson, Snorri, 37

sublimatory, 67

Sufiism, 28, 29, 31, 42, 154

*Suggestive Enquiry into the Hermetic Mystery* (Atwood), 127, 128

sulphur, 24, 34, 68, 176, 203
   constituent of all metals, 34, 43, 176, 180
   as feminine, 79
   as spirit, 180
   associated with Sol, 202
   red tincture, 202
   – of the Art, 171
   – of the Philosophers, 171, 202

sulphur–*continued*
   Natural –, 170
   Perfected –, 24

sun (Sol), 2, 37, 141, 170, 171
   associated with gold, 5, 73, 157
   symbol of, 24, 102

Sweden, 116

Swedenborg, Emanuel, 122, 124, 125

Syria, 7, 21, 28, 29, 40

*Tabula Smaragdina (Emerald Tablet)*, 2, 6, 7, 22, 93, 155, 159, 172

talismans, 43

Taoism, 159

tarnishing of metals, 5

tartar, 67

Taylor, F. Sherwood, 23, 24

Tehuti, *see* Thoth, Hermes Trismegistus

*Theatrum Chemicum*, 38, 171, 172

Thebes, Egypt, 121

theosophy, 120, 126

Thirty Years' War, 93, 94, 175

Thoth (Tehuti), identified with Adam, 159–60
   with Hermes, 7
   texts ascribed to, 30
   *see also* Hermes Trismegistus

*Thrice Holy Trinosophie* (St Germain), 115, 121–2, 201

Thuringia, 179

time, 25, 142

timing of experiment, 70, 72

tin, 5, 68

tinctures, red and white, 177, 202 *see also* elixir

*Tractatus Aristotelis ad Alexandrum*, 67, 168

transmutant given by stranger, 74, 100–3

transmutation, 32, 70, 92, 178–9
   possibility of, 41, 74, 143, 205–6
   theories of, 75
   gold from brass, 45
      from copper, 45, 92, 106
      from lead, 74, 95, 103, 113
      from mercury, 44, 65, 70, 72, 90, 97, 118
   silver from copper, 106
      from lead, 70, 72
      from mercury, 117–8

*Travels of an Alchemist*, 159

tree of life, 142 *see also* Yggdrasil

tree, philosophical, 183–4

*Turba Philosophorum*, 33

Turkish Empire, 69, 93

Tus, 29

Umayyad dynasty, 29
Unconscious, 73, 79, 122, 143

Valentinus, Basilius, 179, 182, 184
valerian, 67
Valhalla, 142
Vandals, 20
Vaughan, Robert, 184
venereal disease, 179
Venus, 5–6, 68, 141
vessels, alchemical, 23, 31, 37, 67, 70, 140
vial, 67
Vienna, 116
virgin's milk, 171
visions, 25, 73, 79, 122
vitriol, 67, 97, 205
volatile liquids, 201, 204
 — metals, 113, 171
volcanoes, 176

Waite, A. E., 180
Waley, Arthur, 159

water, element, 8, 23, 156
 rubifying, 67
 for albification, 67
 of creation, 141
 of life, 171
 of Paradise, 201
wax, 74, 96, 103–4, 178, 202
wind, 2
witches, 94
wolf, grey, 77
world-serpent (Ouroboros), 24, 37
wort, brewer's, 67
Wotan, 21
Württemberg, Duke of, 96

yeast, 67
Yggdrasil, 37, 142
Yin and Yang, 24

zodiacal signs, 70
Zoroastrianism, 153
Zosimus, 23, 25, 28, 159

In this scholarly and lively survey of the work of alchemists through the centuries, C. A. Burland brilliantly unravels the strange mixture of psychology, philosophy, mysticism, and chemistry which makes up the alchemical arts. Although alchemists have often been derided as charlatans, this account reveals that many of them, from ancient Egypt to our own day, have engaged in a serious and dedicated search for the inner meaning of the whole material universe.

In its deeper implications, alchemy is a philosophy amounting almost to a religion. The alchemists have firmly believed that the secret to the making of gold would be revealed by a power from above as a seal of approval, a symbolic reward for a lifetime of work and study.

"The quest," as C. A. Burland observes, "brought its own satisfaction. The alchemist made a contribution to the knowledge of the human mind as great as his contribution to the development of scientific chemistry. To accompany him in the study of his mysterious art is fascinating, because we follow a group of people who have transmitted to our modern times some of the knowledge and mystery of the ancient world."

*The Arts of the Alchemists* is documented with a wealth of magnificent plates, 8 in color and 130 in black and white, selected from a wide variety of manuscripts and treatises and, in many instances, reproduced here for the first time.

| | | |
|---|---|---|
| Acetū | ✚ | Vinegar of Beere |
| Acetū vini. | ✚ | Wine vineger. |
| Acetū distil. ated. | ⌒ ✚ ✚ | |
| Calx. | Ψ ʊ | Lime. |
| Salx viva. | CV. ℃ | unslaked lime. |
| chalibs. | ♄→ ℔ | steele |
| Ignis, | △ . | |
| Aqua Regis. | ▽R ▽℞ | Aqua that dividef gold. |